BTEC Tech Award

SPORT, ACTIVITY AND FITNESS

Student Book

Jenny Stafford-Brown

Published by Pearson Education Limited, 80 Strand, London, WC2R 0RL.

www.pearsonschoolsandfecolleges.co.uk

Copies of official specifications for all Pearson qualifications may be found on the website: qualifications.pearson.com

Text © Pearson Education Limited 2019
Typeset by PDQ Digital Media Solutions
Original illustrations © Pearson Education Limited 2019
Picture research by SPi-Global
Cover illustration by Jo Goodberry, KJA Artists

First published 2019

22 21 20 19
10 9 8 7 6 5 4 3 2 1

British Library Cataloguing in Publication Data
A catalogue record for this book is available from the British Library

ISBN 978 1 446 94362 5

Printed in Slovakia by Neografia

Acknowledgements
The publisher would like to thank the following for their kind permission to reproduce copyright material.

Text
The publisher would like to thank the following for their kind permission to reproduce their material.

26 Elsevier : Davis B et al: Physical Education and the Study of Sport; 2000

Photographs
The publisher would like to thank the following for their kind permission to reproduce their photographs.

(Key: b-bottom; c-centre; l-left; r-right; t-top)

123RF: Aleksandr Davydov 25, Deklofenak 28, Sjenner13 31, Wabeno 33t, lsantilli 35t, Jagdish Agarwal 36t, Vereshchagin Dmitry 52, robynmac 106; **Alamy Stock Photo:** Action Plus Sports Images 2, Jeff Morgan 13 21, Frances M. Roberts 30, John Fryer 13, PHOVOIR 38, Hongqi Zhang 61, Bon Appetit 67, michael simons 114, Hero Images Inc. 5, dov makabaw 41 David Whinham 44, Panther Media GmbH 56; **Getty Images:** Popperfoto 38t, Bettmann 40, Sidekick/E+ 53, Matthew Ashton/Corbis Sport 55, Guido Mieth 4, Brendon Thorne/Stringer 17, Phil Sheldon/Popperfoto/Contributor 23; **Shutterstock:** Richman Photo 8, Ivan Kochergin 11, AXL 28, Tom Wang 18, Konmesa 6, Presseye/INPHO 11, Paolo Bona 14t, CatJB 14b, Andrey_Popov 26, Chad Zuber 27, Merla 29, 5 C-You 33b, Clive Limpkin/Associated Newspapers 35t, Sipa USA 36b, Vitalii Nesterchuk 38b, Chris Curtis 39, Billion Photos 42t, Nattawit Khomsanit 42b, Vladimir Zhoga 45, Sportpoint 52, Eddie Keogh for The FA 1, ifong 4, Zai Aragon 7, Yin Bogu 10, Ulrik Pedersen 10, CP DC Press 11, Diego Barbieri 12, Gorodenkoff 15, Watchares Hansawek 22, Syda Productions 34, wavebreakmedia 39, Rawpixel 41, HconQ 52, HandmadePictures 83, Valeria Aksakova 86, Ljupco Smokovski 97, photogl 99, matimix 106, Alisa Khomulo 10, Denys Kurbatov 10, wavebreakmedia 12, Melinda Nagy 21, Undrey 26, Harry Laub/imageBROKER 34, Salvatore Di Nolfi/EPA 37, Gallo Images 40, Kzenon 43, Zarya Maxim Alexandrovich 54, Syda Productions 70, koonsiri boonnak 72, Eurobanks 78, DGLimages.

Cover images: Front: KJA Artists, Back: stockyimages/Shutterstock.com

All other images © Pearson Education with thanks to David Spencer.

Contents

CONTENTS

About this book

This book is designed to support you when you are taking a BTEC Tech Award in Sport, Activity and Fitness.

About your BTEC Tech Award

Congratulations on choosing a BTEC Tech Award in Sport, Activity and Fitness. This exciting and challenging course will introduce you to the sport, activity and fitness sector. By studying for your Award you will gain the important knowledge, understanding and skills that are the foundations for working in this area. To prepare you for working in this sector you will learn about the functions of the body in relation to sport and activity and the principles of training, nutrition and psychology. You will also learn about the different fitness tests, methods of training, and supporting technology that can be used. You will also have the opportunity to apply your learning by planning and implementing your own sessions plans for different groups of people.

How you will be assessed

You will be assessed in two different ways. Components 1 and 3 are assessed through internal assessment. This means that your teacher will give you an assignment brief and indicate to you the deadline for completing it. The assignment will cover what you have been learning about and will be an opportunity to apply your knowledge and skills. You teacher will mark your assignment and award you with a grade. Your assessment for Component 2 will be an external assessment. This will be an external assessment that is set and marked by Pearson. You will have a set time in which to complete this external assessment. The external assessment will be an opportunity to bring together what you have learned in Components 1 and 3.

About the author

Jenny Stafford-Brown

Jenny is a current practitioner in sport related vocational education in the FE sector and has over 20 years' experience in this field. She has a wealth of experience of writing teacher and student resources including text books, teaching materials and national online resources. Jenny also works as a national and international trainer, holds a number of senior assessment roles including chief examiner and senior standards verifier for other qualifications, and is a subject expert for Ofqual.

How to use this book

The book has been designed in a way that will help you to easily navigate through your course. Each component from the course is covered in a separate chapter that makes clear what you are learning and how this will contribute to your assessment. There are opportunities for you to test your understanding of key areas, as well as activities that will challenge and extend your knowledge and skills. You will get the most from this book if you use each feature as part of your study. The different features will also help you develop the skills that will be important in completing your assignments as well as preparing you for your external assessment.

Features of the book

This book is designed in spreads, which means that each pair of facing pages represents a topic of learning. Each spread is about 1 hour of lesson time. Your teacher may ask you to work through a spread during a lesson or in your own time. Each spread contains a number of features that will help you to check what you are learning and offer opportunities to practise new skills.

Getting started A short activity or discussion that will introduce you to what you will be covering in the lesson.

Link it up This indicates where what you're learning about is covered in another part of the course.

Key terms Important words or terms are defined.

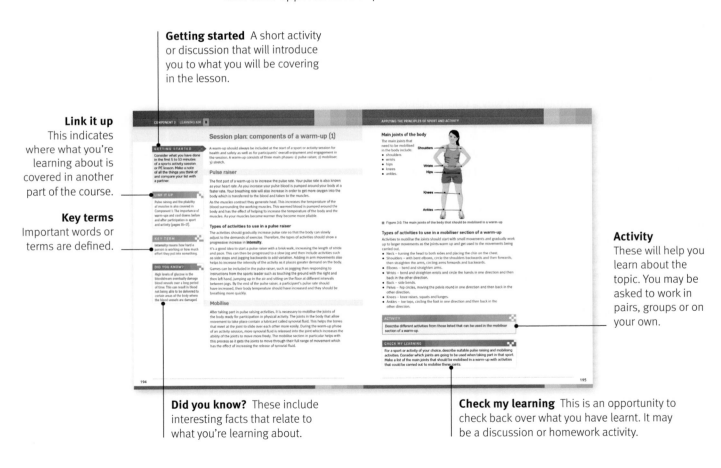

Activity These will help you learn about the topic. You may be asked to work in pairs, groups or on your own.

Did you know? These include interesting facts that relate to what you're learning about.

Check my learning This is an opportunity to check back over what you have learnt. It may be a discussion or homework activity.

At the end of each learning aim there is a section that outlines how you will be assessed and provides opportunities for you to build skills for assessment.

Checkpoint This feature is designed to allow you to assess your learning. The 'strengthen' question helps you to check your knowledge and understanding of what you have been studying, while the 'challenge' questions are an opportunity to extend your learning.

Assessment Activity This is a practice assessment that reflects the style and approach of an assignment brief. In Component 2, tasks in the assessment activity features will be similar to those you should expect in your external assessment.

Tip A hint or tip that will help you with your assessment.

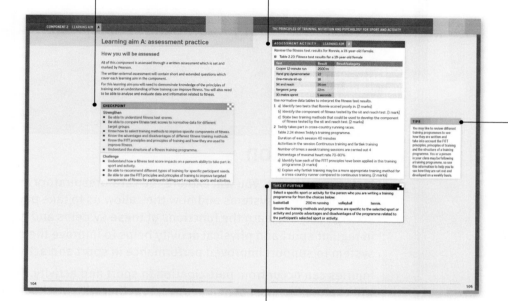

Take it further This provides suggestions for what you can do to further the work you've done in the practice assessment.

01

Understand the Body and the Supporting Technology for Sport and Activity

Introduction

In this component, you will explore the cardiorespiratory and musculoskeletal systems and how they allow us to take part in sport and activity. You will learn the functions of these systems and how participation in regular sport and physical activity helps to improve the efficiency of each system to support improved performance in sport and activity.

Injuries can occur from participation in sport and activity. This component will explore the most common ones, together with methods to help reduce the risk of injury. You will also explore methods that can be used to treat a sports injury and to help to reduce the negative effects of injury. Methods to increase the rate of recovery will also be explored, including the use of new technology to support rehabilitation.

Lastly, the use of technology in sport and activity has increased substantially over the last few years and this will be explored in relation to equipment, protection, clothing, footwear, facilities and computer-related devices.

LEARNING AIMS

In this component you will:

A	Investigate the impact of sport and activity on the body systems
B	Explore common injuries in sport and activity and methods of rehabilitation
C	Understand the use of technology for sport and activity.

The structure of the cardiorespiratory system

The cardiorespiratory system is made up of two body systems:

1 cardiovascular system
2 respiratory system.

These two systems work together to take oxygen into the body and then deliver it to the body's tissues. They also work together to remove waste products.

Structure of the cardiovascular system

The cardiovascular system consists of the heart, blood vessels and blood. The heart is made up of four chambers: two chambers are called **atria**; the other two chambers are called **ventricles**.

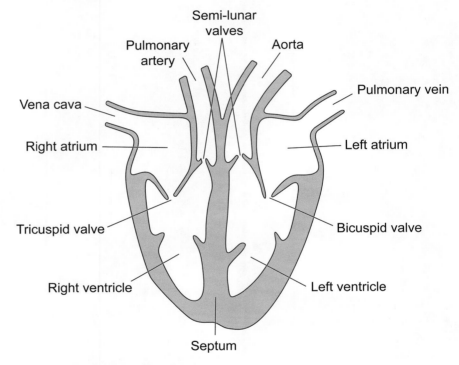

◘ **Figure 1.1: Structure of the heart**

The atria are positioned at the top of the heart and receive blood from either the lungs or the body. The ventricles are below the atria and pump blood to either the lungs or the body.

The heart is divided into a right side and a left side. The septum is a wall of tissue that separates the right-hand side from the left-hand side of the heart. The right atrium receives blood from the body via the vena cava and the right ventricle pumps blood through the pulmonary **artery** to the lungs. The left atrium receives oxygenated blood from the lungs via the pulmonary **vein** and pumps blood.

Valves are positioned between the atria and ventricles to ensure blood flows in the right direction by preventing back flow of blood from the ventricles to the atria. The tricuspid valve is located between the right atrium and right ventricle. The bicuspid valve is located between the left atrium and left ventricle.

■ = deoxygenated blood

■ = oxygenated blood

◘ **Figure 1.2: The cardiovascular system showing the heart and blood vessels that together form the cardiovascular system**

Structure of the respiratory system

The respiratory system consists of the lungs and the airways leading to and from the lungs and the diaphragm, which is a muscle.

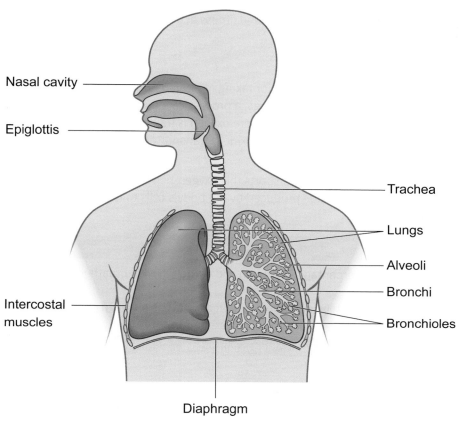

■ Figure 1.3: Structure of the respiratory system

The functions of the cardiorespiratory system

GETTING STARTED

The cardiorespiratory system consists of the cardiovascular system and the respiratory system. List as many functions as you can think of that are carried out by the cardiovascular and respiratory systems.

KEY TERMS

Inspiration means breathing air in.

Expiration means breathing air out.

Individually the cardiovascular and the respiratory systems perform important functions that enable your body to work. They also work together to perform important functions for everyday life, and in sport and fitness activities.

Gaseous exchange

The respiratory system is responsible for taking in oxygen through breathing in. This process is called **inspiration**. In the lungs, a process called gaseous exchange takes place. Gaseous exchange is a process where oxygen is transferred to the bloodstream (known as oxygen uptake) and carbon dioxide is transported from the blood into the lungs and breathed out.

The cardiovascular system then transports this oxygen-rich blood around the body and brings carbon dioxide produced by the body's cells to the lungs through **expiration**.

ACTIVITY

Table 1.1 shows the percentage of oxygen and carbon dioxide breathed in and out.

▫ **Table 1.1 The percentage of oxygen, carbon dioxide and nitrogen gas in inhaled and exhaled air**

Gas	Percentage in inhaled air	Percentage in exhaled air
Oxygen	21	16
Carbon dioxide	0.04	4
Nitrogen	79	79

1 Explain why the percentage of oxygen in inhaled air is different from the percentage in exhaled air.

2 Explain why the percentage of carbon dioxide in inhaled air is different from the percentage in exhaled air.

3 Describe why you think the percentage of inhaled and exhaled nitrogen is the same.

Removing waste products

The process of producing energy for muscle contraction produces waste products such as lactic acid and carbon dioxide. If these waste products build up in the muscle tissue they will stop the muscle from working. The cardiovascular system removes these waste products from the muscles in the bloodstream.

Clotting wounds

KEY TERM

Clot – also known as a scab which forms over wounded tissue to prevent excess blood loss from damaged blood vessels.

Platelets are a component of blood which are transported all around the body. If a person cuts themselves, platelets from the bloodstream gather around the wound to produce a **clot** which stops the wound from bleeding, preventing the body from losing too much blood.

Regulating temperature

The cardiovascular system helps to maintain a consistent body temperature (also known as thermoregulation) through **vasodilation** and **vasoconstriction** of blood vessels.

In hot conditions, blood vessels close to the skin surface vasodilate; this means they get larger so more blood flows through them. As these blood vessels are located close to the skin surface, heat can be lost from the blood flowing through these vessels to the surrounding environment. This process helps to lose heat from the body. However, in cold conditions blood vessels close to the skin surface vasoconstrict. This reduces the blood flow to the skin which means less heat from the blood is lost to the surrounding environment, helping to keep the person warm.

KEY TERMS

Vasodilation – vaso means blood vessel, dilation means increase in size.

Vasoconstriction refers to a decrease in the size of a blood vessel.

◩ **After exercise, the blood vessels dilate close to the skin surface.**

CHECK MY LEARNING

Describe what is meant by gaseous exchange and explain how the cardiovascular and respiratory systems work together to supply the body with oxygen and remove waste products.

Musculoskeletal system

The musculoskeletal system is made up of two body systems:

1 muscular system

2 skeletal system.

These two systems work together to allow movement of the body.

Muscular system

The muscular system consists of all the muscles in the body.

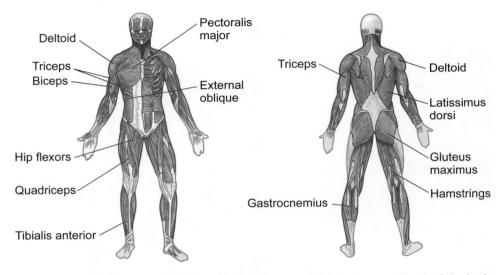

□ Figure 1.4: The muscular system showing the muscles in the front and back of the body

Skeletal system

The skeletal system consists of bones and ligaments. This system allows movement at joints, which is where two or more bones meet.

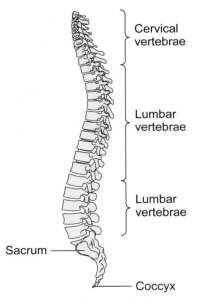

□ Figure 1.5: The vertebral column

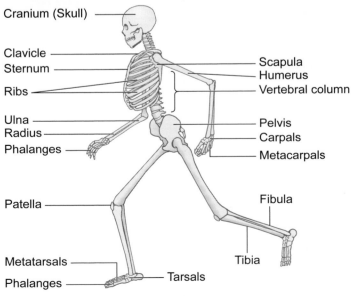

□ Figure 1.6: The human skeleton consists of bones

Functions of the musculoskeletal system

Protection of vital organs

The main function of some of the bones of the skeleton is to protect the structures that are located beneath them. The cranium protects the brain from getting damaged when there is an impact to the head such as when taking a header in football.

Joints

A joint is formed where two or more bones meet, such as the knee, the elbow and the shoulder. Bones being joined in this manner allows for much more movement than if an arm, for example, consisted of just one long bone. There are many joints in the body and some allow more movement than others.

ACTIVITY

Consider the following joints in your body:

1 wrist

2 elbow

3 shoulder.

Which joint allows the greatest range of movement?

Give examples of different sporting movements that occur at each joint, such as bowling a cricket ball which uses the shoulder joint.

Which joint allows the smallest range of movement?

Movement

Muscles attach to the bones of the skeleton by tendons. When a muscle contracts it pulls on the bone, which makes the bone move. This whole process allows us to move our body in various ways.

Ligaments

Ligaments are tissues that join bone to bone. Their function is to keep a joint stable so that it allows the right amount of movement but keeps the joint in place.

When two or more bones in a joint are displaced this is called a dislocation. It can be very painful when a joint is dislocated.

Produce platelets, red and white blood cells

The bones in the skeleton also produce key components of the blood. Platelets are produced, which are responsible for clotting blood. Red blood cells are produced which carry oxygen around the body. White blood cells are produced which help to fight infections.

◻ When a joint is dislocated, such as the knee, it is very painful.

CHECK MY LEARNING

1 Identify how muscles are attached to the skeleton.

2 Explain the function of ligaments.

3 Describe the key components of blood.

The effect of regular participation in sport and activity on components of fitness

Fitness is a complicated subject. Many people consider it to be simply how far we can run, swim, cycle or row. However, fitness consists of several different parts or components. For example, the distance a person can complete is only a part of the overall elements that make someone fit. A person can have high levels of fitness in one area of fitness and low levels of fitness in another area.

Effect of regular participation on a participant's components of fitness

Regular participation in sport and activity is classed as usually at least three times per week for a minimum six-week period. This type of participation has a positive effect on the component(s) of fitness that is (are) being trained during the sport or activity session and will help the person to become more effective in that sport or activity each time they participate.

Aerobic exercise

Aerobic means 'requiring air' and aerobic activities increase your breathing and heart rates.

Long-term training is classed as regular participation in sport or exercise for at least six weeks.

Cardiovascular fitness is increased by taking part in these types of sport and activities. Cardiovascular fitness is the ability to exercise continuously for a certain period of time without becoming tired. Cardiovascular fitness therefore means that the cardiorespiratory system can work efficiently, supplying nutrients and oxygen to working muscles during sustained physical activity.

Muscular endurance can also be improved from taking part in aerobic exercises. Muscular endurance is related to how efficiently your muscular system works. The greater a person's muscular endurance, the increased ability they have to perform an exercise that involves repetitive contractions of a muscle over an extended period of time.

Because there are many muscles in our body, it is possible to have good muscular endurance in some muscle groups but poor muscular endurance in others. For example, a person that takes part in cycling will gain improved muscular endurance in their leg muscles but their arm muscles are not exercised in the sport so these muscles will not develop muscular endurance.

Body composition can be improved by regular participation in aerobic sport and activity, as this type of activity will use calories for the repeated muscle contractions. The longer a person carries out aerobic sports or activities, the more calories they will use. This will help prevent any excess calories consumed being stored as body fat. If a person wants to lose excess body fat, participation in aerobic sports and activities combined with a calorie-controlled diet will help them to lose excess body fat, which will therefore help to improve body composition.

Resistance exercise

Resistance exercise is a form of sport or activity where you are working against some type of force that 'resists' your movement, such as lifting weights or pulling on elastic resistance bands.

Muscular strength is increased from taking part in regular resistance exercise.

■ The larger the muscle mass, the more strength the person has.

Strength is related to how much muscle mass a person has – the larger the muscle mass, the more strength the person has. This is because muscle tissue produces force. Force is any interaction that, if not stopped, will change the motion of an object. Force is measured in newtons (N), named after Sir Isaac Newton. One newton is the force needed to move 1 kg of mass at a rate of 1 metre per second squared.

The more muscle tissues a person has, the more force their muscles can produce.

To increase muscular strength through training, it is necessary to have a high resistance with low repetitions in relation to how many times the resistance is lifted.

ACTIVITY

Identify individual sports and team sports that require high levels of strength.

For each sport, describe why the person playing that sport needs high levels of strength to perform well.

While it is not necessary to have high levels of strength for health reasons, a certain level of strength is required to support daily activities. Strong postural muscles are required to keep an upright stance and prevent back pains. Strong leg muscles are required to allow us to hold our body weight and move around.

Muscular endurance can also be improved by **resistance training**. To train for muscular endurance it is necessary to have low resistance and complete a high number of repetitions.

Body composition can also be improved by increasing muscle mass. This is because muscle tissue has a high metabolic rate when compared with other body tissues so it does help to 'burn calories' to prevent a person from becoming overweight. It is also important to note that as a person gets older, from about the age of 30, their muscle mass naturally starts to reduce unless the person takes part in resistance training to try and maintain or increase their muscle mass.

KEY TERMS

Strength is the maximum force (in kg or N) that can be generated by a muscle or muscle group during a single contraction.

Resistance training is undertaking exercise or activity to improve muscular strength and/or endurance by using weights, your own bodyweight or, for example, elastic bands, to provide resistance to the muscles.

CHECK MY LEARNING

Collect the views generated by the class on what fitness means to them. List the different ideas and compare them to what fitness means to you.

Physiological impact of engagement in sport and activity on the body systems

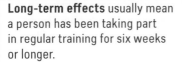

DID YOU KNOW?

It is reported that Chris Froome, who has won the Tour de France four times, has a resting heart rate of 29 bpm.

KEY TERMS

Long-term effects usually mean a person has been taking part in regular training for six weeks or longer.

Cardiac hypertrophy is where the heart muscle increases in size.

Left ventricle – pumps blood to tissues all over the body. The right ventricle only pumps blood to the lungs.

Blood pressure – the heart pumps the blood through a system of blood vessels which needs to be at a certain pressure to ensure that the blood is able to travel all around the body and return back to the heart.

Long-term effects of exercise on the cardiorespiratory system

The main changes that occur to the cardiorespiratory system through taking part in regular aerobic sports or physical activities are concerned with increasing the body's capability to uptake oxygen and deliver it to the working muscles.

Cardiac hypertrophy

The heart is a muscle. Just as with skeletal muscles, if the heart muscle is exercised it will increase in size. If you were to dissect the heart of a top aerobic endurance athlete, you would find that the walls of the **left ventricle** are markedly thicker than those of a person who did not perform regular aerobic exercise.

An increase in heart size can result in greater oxygen intake, resulting in more efficient delivery to the working muscles.

Drop in resting heart rate

Because the heart increases in size it is able to pump out more blood each time it beats – this is called the stroke volume. As the stroke volume is increased, the heart no longer needs to beat as often to get the same amount of blood around the body. This results in a decrease in resting heart rate, as the heart is working more efficiently.

Drop in resting blood pressure

The force of your heart pumping blood around your body is called **blood pressure**. If blood was not pumped under some sort of pressure, then it would not make its way all around the body and back to your heart.

High blood pressure values can be harmful to a person's health; however, taking part in regular aerobic sport and physical activity can decrease resting blood pressure.

This happens through a combination of a reduced resting heart rate and because the blood vessels become more elastic due to the temporary increased blood flow through them when exercising. The blood vessels can then expand to a greater extent so there is a reduced resistance to blood flow in general, reducing blood pressure.

Increase in red blood cells

Exercise can result in an increase in red blood cells. The main function of red blood cells is to transport oxygen to the body cells. The increased need for oxygen during vigorous exercise stimulates your body to create more red blood cells. By having a greater number of red blood cells in the blood, more oxygen can be transported to the body cells which can then be used for energy production.

Drop in blood viscosity

Plasma is the watery fluid in blood, and the more plasma there is, the less viscous (thick) the blood becomes. An adaptation to regular aerobic sport or physical activity means an increase in plasma volume. This helps the blood to flow more easily in the blood vessels as it is less thick and will therefore have the effect of decreasing blood pressure, which is beneficial to a person's health.

Increased vital capacity

Vital capacity increases through regular participation in aerobic sport or physical activity. The increased strength of the respiratory muscles is partly responsible for this as it aids lung inflation and deflation.

Improved efficiency of gaseous exchange

Gaseous exchange takes place between the lungs and the bloodstream, and at the muscle tissues and the bloodstream.

Capillaries are the blood vessels in which gaseous exchange takes place. Lots of capillaries are located around the tiny air sacs in the lungs, called alveoli. Oxygen **diffuses** from the alveoli across the capillaries and into the bloodstream, and carbon dioxide diffuses from the blood into the lungs.

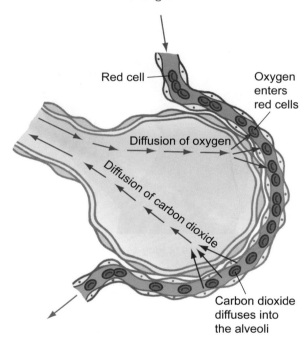

Red cell

Oxygen enters red cells

Diffusion of oxygen

Diffusion of carbon dioxide

Carbon dioxide diffuses into the alveoli

■ Figure 1.7: The process of gaseous exchange

At the muscles, the oxygen from the blood diffuses out of the capillaries and into the muscles and carbon dioxide diffuses into the bloodstream.

Regular participation in sport or physical activity increases the **capillarisation** around the alveoli in the lungs and in the muscle tissues. The increase in capillaries helps to increase the rate of gas exchange and, therefore, increase the amount of oxygen entering the blood and the amount of carbon dioxide leaving the blood.

This improves the oxygen flow to the working muscles and the removal of waste products, so the muscles have more energy and tire less quickly.

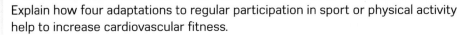

CHECK MY LEARNING

Explain how four adaptations to regular participation in sport or physical activity help to increase cardiovascular fitness.

ACTIVITY

The vital capacity of an average healthy adult is between 3 to 5 litres. Find out the vital capacity of an athlete who takes part in aerobic sports or physical activities.

KEY TERMS

Blood viscosity is the thickness of the blood. Viscosity is how thick a liquid is. For example, water has a very low viscosity but syrup has a high viscosity.

Vital capacity is the amount of air that can be forced out of the lungs after **maximal inspiration**.

Maximal inspiration is the most amount of air that a person can breathe in during a breath.

Gaseous exchange is the process of oxygen diffusing into or out of the bloodstream and carbon dioxide diffusing into or out of the bloodstream.

Diffusion is the free movement of particles from areas of high concentration to areas of low concentration.

Capillarisation is the process where new capillaries are formed at the alveoli in the lungs and at the skeletal muscle.

Physiological impact of regular participation in sport and physical activity on the musculoskeletal system

Long-term effects of exercise on the musculoskeletal system

The main changes that occur to the musculoskeletal system through taking part in regular resistance sports or physical activities are concerned with increasing the strength of the musculoskeletal system.

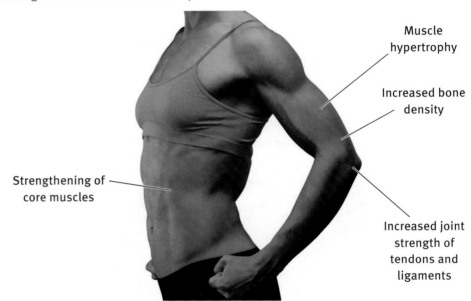

Muscle hypertrophy

Increased bone density

Increased joint strength of tendons and ligaments

Strengthening of core muscles

■ The musculoskeletal system adapts to long-term exercise mainly by increasing in strength.

Increased bone density

Bones are continually being remodelled where old bone cells are removed and new bone cells are laid down. Minerals are used in the remodelling process and are used when new bone cells are formed to make the bones stronger and denser – this means they will be less likely to break on impact such as when a person falls over.

Taking part in regular resistance or weight bearing sports or physical activities increases the rate of bone remodelling and increases the amount of minerals laid down in the process, which has the effect of increasing bone density.

Increased joint strength of tendons and ligaments

A joint is where two bones meet. **Ligaments** hold bones together; therefore, the stronger the ligaments holding the two bones together, the stronger the joint is going to be. Strong **tendons** are also beneficial as they help to prevent sports injuries as well as contributing to a person's overall strength.

Regular participation in resistance or weight bearing sports and physical activities will increase the strength of tendons and ligaments.

 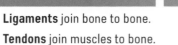

Muscle hypertrophy

Muscle hypertrophy occurs when a muscle is stressed through lifting heavy weights. The muscle tissue experiences very small tears called micro tears. These stimulate the muscle tissue to rebuild so that it is bigger and therefore stronger than before. If this process is repeated, the muscle tissue will continue to increase in size and strength.

Strengthening of core muscles

Core muscles are very important to maintain a person's posture and help to improve balance and stability. Posture is the way a person stands and holds their body. Good posture helps in sporting and physical activities as it can help keep bones and ligaments in the correct position. This means that the muscles are being used most efficiently and decreases the stress on joints and ligaments.

ACTIVITY

The following activity, called 'the plank', helps to train the core muscles.

1 Lie out horizontally with toes on floor, stomach down.

2 Push yourself up so your forearms are in contact with the floor from hands to elbow. Keep your back straight. Maintain this position for between 20 seconds to 1 minute dependent on fitness. Repeat the exercise after a rest.

The plank will strengthen abdominal muscles and erector spinae as well as utilising muscles in the arms, shoulders, chest and legs.

◨ The plank exercise strengthens the core muscles.

CHECK MY LEARNING

There are numerous sports that benefit from an athlete having increased muscular endurance and increased strength. Create a list of three individual sports and three team sports. For each sport, describe how at least one long-term effect of regular participation in resistance sports or physical activities is beneficial to the sports person taking part in that sport.

Learning aim A: assessment practice

How you will be assessed

Now that you have studied the topics in Learning aim A you will need to show that you understand the cardiorespiratory and musculoskeletal systems, common sports injuries and the technological advances that impact on sport and activity.

Your research will need to focus on the structures of the cardiorespiratory and musculoskeletal systems and the long-term adaptation to these body systems as a result of participation in sport and activity.

CHECKPOINT

Strengthen
- Explain the structures of the cardiovascular system and musculoskeletal system.
- Outline the long-term physiological adaptations from taking part in regular sport and activity.
- Explain the benefits of physiological adaptations to participation in sport and activity.

Challenge
- Compare and contrast how participation in different types of sport will lead to adaptations of the cardiovascular system and musculoskeletal system.
- Give justified reasons why regular participation in sport and activity can improve performance in two different sports or activities.

ASSESSMENT ACTIVITY   LEARNING AIM   A

- Take the pulse rate for 1 minute of a person who you know takes part in regular sport and activity that lasts for 30 minutes or longer, such as long-distance running.

- Repeat with a person who you know takes part in resistance-based sports and activities such as weight lifting.

- Compare the heart rates and explain the difference between the two, considering physiological adaptations from participation in the two different types of sports or activities.

- Explain how the musculoskeletal system will have adapted to long-term participation in weight lifting.

- Explain how physiological adaptations from long-term participation in sport or activity would improve performance in a sport of your choice.

TIPS

It is not always possible to take the pulse of two different people who take part in regular sport and activity and who meet the requirements in the assessment activity. In this case, you may need to carry out research online to find the resting pulse rate of two well-known sports participants who take part in long-distance running or cycling, for example, and someone who takes part in resistance-based sports or activities.

TAKE IT FURTHER

Carry out research to find out about extreme sport or activity challenges such as ultra-distance marathons. Find out what sort of distances people have to cover and the time frames they complete this in.

Also, find out the weight lifting records for categories of your choice. How does the weight lifted compare to the person's bodyweight?

Explain how physiological adaptations have enabled these participants to accomplish these physical challenges.

The importance of warm-ups and cool downs before and after participation in sport and activity

Warm-up

A warm-up includes activities to gradually increase your heart rate such as going from a fast walk to a slow jog and then increasing the pace of the jog so that blood is pumped around your body at a faster rate. Your breathing rate will also increase in order to get more oxygen into the body, which is transferred to the blood and taken to the muscles.

ACTIVITY

Find your pulse on your wrist or your neck.

▫ Figure 1.8: The pulse can be taken at the wrist or the neck

Use a clock or timer to time 60 seconds. During this time, count your pulse rate and make a note of it in the table.

Now make a note of how many times you breathe in over a one minute period and make a note of it in the table.

Now take part in a five minute pulse raising activity such as moving from a walk to a fast walk then up to a jog.

As soon as you have stopped your activity, find and take your pulse for one minute. Write the number in the table.

After five minutes rest, take part in another pulse raising activity and as soon as you stop, record how many times you breathe in for one minute and write this number in the table.

	Pulse rate (beats per minute)	Breathing rate (breaths per minute)
Rate before taking part in a pulse raising activity		
Rate after taking part in a pulse raising activity		

Compare your results with the rest of the class to find the average resting heart rate and breathing rates, and average pulse rates and breathing rates after taking part in the pulse raising activities.

As the muscles contract they generate heat. This increases the temperature of the blood surrounding the working muscles. As your muscles become warmer they become more **pliable**, which reduces the risk of injury. This means they are less likely to tear when they are stretched when taking part in sport or activity.

ACTIVITY

Get a piece of modelling clay or reusable adhesive putty the size of a 10 pence piece. Using two hands, pull the clay/putty and see what happens to it – how quickly does it break? Now, roll the clay/putty in your hands so that it warms up. After a few minutes of rolling and warming up the clay/putty, try pulling it apart again. What happens to it? How has heating the clay/putty affected its pliability?

The warm-up also increases the production of synovial fluid. Synovial fluid is located between the bones of a synovial joint, such as the ankle or shoulder, which acts as a lubricant. This means that it helps the bones to slide over each other more easily. During the warm-up phase of an activity session, more synovial fluid is released into the joints, which increases the ability of the joints to move more freely. This helps to reduce the risk of joint injuries.

Cool down

After taking part in a sport or activity session, it is important to then perform a cool down, which is a series of stretches or light activity designed to gradually decrease your heart and breathing rate and return your cardiorespiratory system to pre-exercise levels.

During physical activity, movements are due to muscles contracting. When a muscle contracts it will usually get shorter to produce the force required to move a specific part of the body. Some are used continually, e.g. when a person is running, the hamstrings and quadriceps are repeatedly contracting. Once a person stops exercising, the muscles can remain in a slightly contracted state, which means they are a little shorter than before. The more exercise sessions a person takes part in on a regular basis, the more contracted the muscles will become if they are not stretched after participation, which will result in the muscles getting shorter in length. This will eventually result in a decrease in their flexibility and an increased risk of straining a muscle.

To help to reduce this shortening of muscles, the cool down stretch is used to return the working muscles back to their resting length to help to maintain flexibility. If muscles become shorter, they are at greater risk of injury through tearing but the cool down helps to prevent this.

CHECK MY LEARNING

In a group, design a poster showing the importance of warm-up and cool down exercises.

Include an explanation of what happens to the body during a warm-up and why this helps to reduce the risk of injury to muscles and joints.

Explain why it is important to carry out a stretch after taking part in sport and activity in relation to reducing the risk of injury.

Common basic sports injuries

A common basic injury is one that can often occur from taking part in sport or activity and has usually been experienced by most people that take part in regular sport or activity. The fact that it is called basic will mean that it will rarely require any professional medical help and can usually be treated at home.

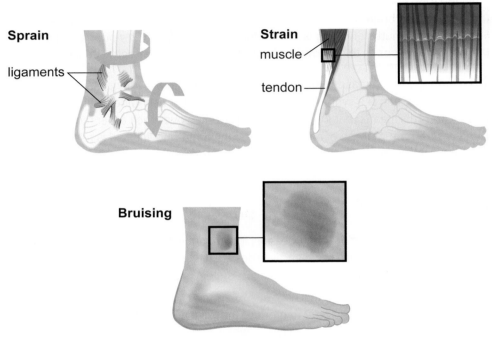

Sprain

ligaments

Strain

muscle

tendon

Bruising

◘ Figure 1.9: Sprains, strains and bruising are common injuries, which are similar but involve different tissue

Sprain

If a person sustains a sprain they will feel immediate pain, which gets worse. Pain and swelling around the sprained joint are the two most common symptoms from a ligament sprain. Some bruising will usually occur at the injury site. The swelling and bruising is the result of torn blood vessels at the injury site, which in turn will produce heat, so the injured area will feel warm to the touch. The injured person will have difficulty moving the sprained joint and if the affected joint is in the lower body, they may not be able to put weight on that joint so might have difficulty walking.

DID YOU KNOW?

A sprain only takes place in a ligament.

A sprain usually occurs from a joint twisting to a greater degree than it should; for example someone playing tennis might turn quickly and go over on their ankle. This movement stretches the ligament too far which results in a tear of the ligament fibres. Sprains often affect the ankles, knees or wrists.

Strain

A strain is a twist or pull of a muscle or tendon which tears the fibres of the affected muscle or tendon. It is often caused by overuse, excessive force or over-stretching when the muscle is pulled too far which results in fibres tearing. Overuse can occur in sports where one part of the body is used repeatedly, such as the elbow in golf. Contact sports like rugby and boxing might result in excessive force. Sudden fast movements, such as at the start of a running race or in long jump, or an overstretched muscle when it has stretched beyond its normal range of motion, can also result in a strain. To help reduce the risk of injury, it is important to warm-up to make the muscles more pliable and to cool down to return muscles to their normal length.

If a person strains a muscle or tendon they will experience swelling, bruising or redness in the affected area. The muscle will feel painful even when it is not being used. There may be weakness of the muscle or tendons. Often the injured person will be unable to move that muscle at all. If a full tear of the muscle fibres occurs, surgical repair may be necessary.

DID YOU KNOW?

A strain only takes place in a muscle.

Bruising

Bruising occurs due to blood vessels being **ruptured** under the skin.

The blood vessels are ruptured usually as a direct result of an external force such as getting hit by a hockey stick or getting kicked from a mistimed tackle in football. The symptoms of a bruise are pain and tenderness around the bruised area, discolouration of the skin which may take time to show, a change in colour over a period of time as the bruise heals, and also possible swelling in the area.

KEY TERM

Rupture means to break or burst. When blood vessels are burst, blood that was being carried in the blood vessels leaks out in the surrounding cells.

ACTIVITY

Draw a table with the column headings shown below. Select three sports of your choice. Complete the table by identifying ways in which a person may experience each of the common types of sports injuries listed.

Sport	Sprain	Strain	Bruise
Squash	Twisting an ankle ligament from turning quickly to run to get to the ball	Straining a muscle from lunging to try and reach a shot	Getting hit by the ball

CHECK MY LEARNING

Create flash cards for each type of basic sports injury to include a strain, a sprain and bruise. The flash cards should contain the name and the symptoms of each injury.

Explain what rupture means and how rupturing of blood vessels results in bruising.

Common complex sports injuries

Common complex sports injuries, like basic injuries, can occur from regular participation in sport and activity but do not happen quite as often as basic sports injuries. Examples are a dislocated joint, a torn ligament or a broken bone. Complex sports injuries will also usually require some professional medical support to treat the injury.

Dislocation

Dislocation is the displacement of a bone from its normal location within a joint. It occurs when a joint is over-stressed, making the bones that meet at that joint disconnect. This might occur through a fall or when the body twists: for instance when playing football a player might keep their foot still on the pitch but twist their body around, causing stress on the knee. Over-stressing the joint like this can cause the joint capsule to tear, together with the ligaments holding the joint in place.

Most dislocations are caused by some form of impact or a fall. If a person has dislocated a joint then it will usually look out of place, deformed and discoloured. They will experience intense pain with numbness and tingling in the affected area. They will not be able to move the dislocated joint.

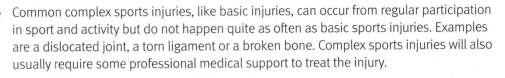

ACTIVITY

Shoulder dislocations can occur in rugby when a person lands awkwardly after being tackled or for a range of other reasons. Carry out research to find out about other joints that can be dislocated from participation in sports. Then complete the table.

Joint	Sport	How dislocation may occur
Finger		
Knee		
Elbow		

Ligament tear

A ligament tear is a severe sprain where the ligament has undergone a great deal of tearing or could be completely torn in two. This can happen in sports where a person suddenly stops, changes direction or performs a jumping movement. Often a popping noise is heard, which is the ligament breaking in half during the tear. There is then immediate swelling around the area where the ligament has been torn and the joint is not stable. The joint will feel hot to the touch as a result of torn blood vessels at the injury site, which will produce heat, and it will be very difficult for the person to move the joint where the ligament tear has occurred.

Fracture

A fracture is the technical term for a broken bone. A fracture results if a bone is hit with enough force to make it break, creating either a small crack or, in a serious fracture, a complete break. It can also occur from overuse.

The symptoms of a fracture include swelling and/or bruising over the fractured bone site, intense pain, loss of function of the fractured bone and an inability to bear weight if bones of the lower limbs are fractured. An open fracture also has a visible bone protruding from the skin.

There are three main types of fracture:
- a stress fracture
- open fracture
- closed fracture.

Stress

A stress fracture is an overuse injury. It occurs when muscles become fatigued and are unable to absorb added shock. Eventually, the fatigued muscle transfers the overload of stress to the bone, causing a tiny crack called a stress fracture. Stress fractures usually occur because of a rapid increase in the amount or intensity of training. The impact of an unfamiliar surface or incorrect trainers can also cause stress fractures.

Open

An open fracture is generally a more serious type of fracture because the broken bone breaks through the skin. The break causes considerable damage to surrounding tissue and can cause serious bleeding if a large artery is ruptured. It also exposes the broken bone to the possibility of infection, which can interfere with healing.

Closed

A closed fracture is where the bone is broken but the broken parts do not break through the skin.

Tendonitis

This is where the tendons of a joint are inflamed.

Tendo**nitis** is usually an overuse injury which leads to an inflammation of the tendon as a result of microtears to the tendon itself. Microtears are small tears in the tendon caused by overuse or repeated injury. Tendonitis can also occur from degeneration of the tendon's collagen as a result of overuse.

The symptoms of tendonitis are pain when moving the joint, tenderness when touching the area that is affected and acute pain.

Shin splints

This is a type of overuse injury that occurs from excessive running on hard surfaces. It can occur if a beginner runner tries to do too much too soon or if an experienced runner substantially increases the distance they run rather than increasing the distance gradually. As the name suggests, the shin bone which is called the tibia is mainly affected. The symptoms of this injury are an aching pain in the shins which increases when exercising. The pain decreases when resting although the person may still feel numbness in their feet and swelling over their shins.

Closed fracture   Open fracture

◘ **Figure 1.10: In a closed fracture the broken bone does not protrude through the skin, but in an open fracture it does**

DID YOU KNOW?

Itis – any words related to injuries that have 'itis' on the end mean inflammation. Many injuries will cause some inflammation so when you see the term 'itis' added to an area of the body this means the area is inflamed, e.g. tendonitis means that a tendon is inflamed.

CHECK MY LEARNING

Explain the difference between a ligament strain and a ligament tear.

Compare and contrast the three different types of bone fracture: stress, open and closed.

Explain the reasons why a beginner runner may suffer from shin splints.

Physiological, psychological and environmental causes of common sporting injuries

Sports injuries can happen for a variety of reasons. These causes generally come under the following categories: physiological, psychological or environmental.

Physiological

Physiological causes relate to the body and how much the person's body is able to cope with the stresses of taking part in sport and activity.

Intensity

Intensity is how hard a person exercises. If a participant exercises or plays sport at too high an intensity they are at a greater risk of injury. This is because they are pushing their body to such an extent that it can result in acute injuries such as a strain or a sprain if they are doing too much too soon. This can also occur over a prolonged period of time because doing too much can result in overuse injuries. An overuse injury can happen when a participant does not take sufficient time for their body to recover after exercise.

Every time we exercise we place our body under stress, which means the body has to repair itself afterwards. If a person does not provide their body with sufficient rest time for it to repair itself, it will become weaker until eventually parts of the body become injured. Also, if we continue to use specific parts of the body over a long period of time the repair is sometimes difficult to manage.

Gravity

Gravity can result in many sports injuries. The effect of gravity means that if you lose your balance when playing sports then you may fall down to the ground. The height from which you fall will have an impact on how severe the sports injury may be. For example, a tackle in football that results in the person tripping over means the person is falling from a standing height to the ground, which will usually result in basic injuries such as getting bruised or a muscle strain. If, however, the person falls from a greater height, such as from a beam in gymnastics, the resulting injury can be more severe, such as a fracture or dislocation of a joint.

The type of sport taken part in can also result in more chances of a person being injured. For example, contact sports such as rugby require players to tackle each other and essentially bring them down, often by grabbing the opponent's legs to trip them over. This means that the tackled player will fall to the ground and the person that tackled them will also fall to the ground. Both players may then suffer some form of potential impact injury from the tackle itself. Other sports are less likely to cause injury such as swimming, as it is a non-contact sport and there are also no issues with gravity other than the dive in entry.

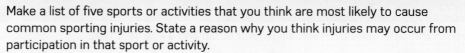

ACTIVITY

Make a list of five sports or activities that you think are most likely to cause common sporting injuries. State a reason why you think injuries may occur from participation in that sport or activity.

Now make a list of five sports or activities that you think are the least likely to cause common sporting injuries. State a reason why you think injuries may not occur from participation in that sport or activity.

Psychological

Psychological causes relate to the mental characteristics of a person and therefore to how they think of themselves and other people.

Low self-confidence

If a person has low self-confidence it means they do not believe in themselves and do not think they are able to perform well, which can result in sporting behaviours that can lead to injury. For example, a person with low self-confidence may not feel that they are capable of tackling an opponent in rugby who they perceive to be much better than they are. They may feel that they should try to tackle that person but do not fully commit to the tackle, which can then result in them getting injured.

Peer pressure

This is where a person is influenced by other people who are similar to that person – peers may be similar in age, social position or have the same ability. People playing together in a sports team for example would be considered peers. Peer pressure can encourage some people to perform a skill that is beyond their ability, which could then result in injury to themselves or to other people. For example, a person who is learning to dive may be encouraged to dive off a higher diving board than they are ready for, which could then result in them getting injured because they are not able to enter the water in the correct way from that height.

Reduced concentration as a result of stress

If an athlete feels stressed it can alter their focus and narrow their attention span which means they do not notice other players. This can make them more likely to make a mistimed football tackle, for example, which can result in injury. Stress can also increase muscle tension which affects a person's coordination and will therefore increase the risk of injury.

 A waterlogged pitch can be hazardous.

Environmental

Environmental conditions are often uncontrollable and can have a big impact on outdoor pursuit-based sports such as mountain climbing or sailing. For other sports, the environment can also impact the safety of participants when taking part in that sport or activity.

Weather

The weather is the main concern related to environmental causes of sports injury. Excessive rain can result in sports fields becoming a dangerous environment to play sport on. An icy or waterlogged field, shown in the photo, has the potential to cause many types of injury. The playing surface can also be hazardous; for example all-weather 3G turf is a more abrasive surface which means it can produce skin abrasions if a player slips and falls onto it.

Temperature

The temperature is also an environmental concern. If it is too hot, this can cause participants to become tired more quickly and can cause problems such as dehydration and heat exhaustion.

If it is too cold, extreme wet and cold weather can lead to hypothermia. Cold weather conditions can also increase the risk of muscle strains.

CHECK MY LEARNING ■ ■

Match the following with either a physiological, psychological or environmental cause of sporting injuries.
- A hot sunny day
- Not fully committing to a tackle
- Peer pressure
- Waterlogged football pitch
- Icy hockey pitch
- Significantly increasing running distance
- Falling after being tackled
- Reduced concentration from stress

Equipment-related causes of common sporting injuries

Equipment

Equipment includes what a person wears to take part in the sport or activity and also the apparatus they use when taking part in the sport or activity.

Inappropriate clothing and footwear

Not having the appropriate clothing or footwear can result in sports injuries. For example, when fell walking, hiking boots are needed to provide the right grip and also stability to the ankle. Wearing footwear with little grip or not enough ankle support increases the risk of the person slipping over or spraining their ankle while walking over uneven ground.

Lack of protective equipment

Protective equipment is worn for specific sports to reduce the risk of some sports injuries. For example, in football, players tackle each other and this process can result in players getting kicked in the shins. Therefore, shin pads are worn to protect the area so that if a person does get kicked they are less likely to have a severely bruised shin. Many sports require the use of a gum shield to help to reduce the risk of teeth being damaged or knocked out as a result of impact from another player or ball, for example. Each sport has clear rules about what protective equipment must be worn by players, such as shin pads in football. However, some protective equipment is optional such as a skull cap in rugby.

◘ A skull cap in rugby is optional protective equipment that can be worn by participants.

ACTIVITY

In the UK, cyclists are not currently required by law to wear cycling helmets. In other countries, such as Australia, a cyclist would be breaking the law if they did not wear a helmet.

Discuss with a partner the advantages of wearing a cycling helmet as well as reasons why people may choose not to wear a helmet when out riding their bikes. Explain if you think it should become a legal requirement to wear a cycling helmet in the UK.

DID YOU KNOW?

Research that has included findings from more than 64000 cyclists strongly suggests that wearing a cycling helmet reduces the risk of a serious head injury by nearly 70%.

Damaged equipment

Sometimes the equipment being used may be damaged which can result in sports injuries. For example, if the springs on a trampoline are not attached properly this could result in the trampoline bed collapsing and in the person using the trampoline suffering an impact with the ground; this could result in a complex sports injury such as a fracture.

■ Damaged or poorly maintained equipment may cause sports injuries.

Incorrect use of equipment

The equipment may be in very good working order; however, if it is not used properly it could result in injury. For example, if a person was taking part in weight training but used weights that were too heavy for them, it could result in a serious strain or sprain. Or if a gym does not carry out a proper induction for new members in how to use the equipment correctly, injury may occur.

ACTIVITY

For the following sports, make a list of the clothing and footwear a person would need to participate in that sport.

Sport	Clothing	Footwear
Scuba diving		
Rock climbing		
100 m sprinting		

Give an explanation for why the clothing and footwear is required for each sport.

CHECK MY LEARNING

For a selected team sport of your choice, describe the clothing, footwear and equipment required to participate in that sport.

Explain what sort of injuries may occur if the required protective equipment was not worn.

Describe how equipment for your selected sport could be broken and the potential injuries this could result in for participants using the equipment.

People-related risks and coaching causes of common sporting injuries

People-related risks

The person taking part in the sport or activity is also responsible for their actions, and in some cases may increase their risk of sustaining a sports injury due to factors related to themselves.

Age

The age of a participant can increase their risk of sustaining certain types of sports injury. For example, younger children taking part in sport are potentially more likely to suffer from injuries that are a result of falling because they are having to learn how to run fast and how to balance their body to avoid tripping over. Also, when children are growing they are still getting used to their arms and legs being longer and have to adjust how they balance themselves and coordinate their body with longer limbs.

As a person gets older they are more likely to become less flexible and more susceptible to muscle and ligament strains unless they carry out a full warm-up and take part in stretching exercises to maintain or improve their flexibility.

Drugs and alcohol

Taking alcohol or any drugs that affect the way the brain works can increase the likelihood of a person getting injured when taking part in sport or activity. If the brain's processing capabilities are reduced, the person is more likely to have slower responses or be unable to move in the way they were able to when not taking drugs or alcohol. This can result in injuries, such as not moving out of the way in time to avoid a ball being thrown towards them. Alcohol also has other negative effects on the body: it impairs muscle growth, dehydrates the body, prevents muscle recovery and can affect memory.

Skill level and experience

Injuries can occur if players play against each other but have very different skill levels or experience. Examples are children playing against adults or elite players competing against recreational players. This is even more important when the sport being played is a contact sport, as elite players will be able to tackle with more force and this may result in the tackled person getting injured as they are not used to dealing with a tackle of such force.

Insufficient warm-up

An insufficient warm-up can lead to reduced flexibility, which will mean the person's range of motion will be reduced. This means that if a person tries to reach out and stretch to a greater degree than they are able to, the muscle tissue will be more likely to tear and the person will suffer from a muscle strain. Ligaments and tendons can also have reduced flexibility without a full warm-up.

Overtraining

If a participant takes part in a training programme that is not appropriate it can lead to sports injuries, through overtraining because the body is not being allowed enough time to recover and adapt. This means the musculoskeletal system becomes weaker and more prone to injury.

Figure 1.11: When lifting a heavy weight from the ground, it is important to bend the knees and keep the back straight. Don't follow the first example above!

Overtraining can occur if:

- the training programme is of an excessive volume and/or intensity
- there is a rapid increase in volume or intensity
- there is a sudden change in the type of training
- the participant trains when they are experiencing excessive fatigue
- they have inadequate rest time between each training session
- they use a faulty technique when training.

A person suffering from overtraining may show symptoms such as: muscle soreness, elevated resting heart rate, increased susceptibility to infections, increased incidence of injuries, irritability, depression, loss of motivation and insomnia.

Coaching

The coach and their coaching methodology can also impact on the likelihood of a participant getting injured when taking part in sport or activity.

Poor training methods

Various training methods are key for all sports participation to help to avoid injury. Core stability training, which means exercises specifically to strengthen the muscles of the back, abdomen and around the pelvis, helps to maintain a good posture which is essential in avoiding injury and issues with how a person moves.

If a coach does not include these types of training then they are putting the participants at risk. The coach should also have up-to-date knowledge of the fitness and skills level of the participant. This will make sure they don't push them too hard and concentrate training on the relevant components of fitness and skills level of the participant.

Unsafe practice and poor technique

Unsafe practice can result from inappropriate instruction given by a coach. It is vital that all instruction is given by someone who has an up-to-date and in-depth knowledge about the sport and the training required to participate and play effectively in that sport. For example, when taking part in strength training, the technique used to complete weight lifting is very important or it could lead to muscle strains or ligament sprains or back injuries (see Figure 1.11).

It is essential that the rules and regulations for the sport, as given by the specific governing body, have been correctly interpreted and are appropriately enforced by the coach. If the coach is very safety conscious and makes the participants aware of potential risks, then they are more likely to follow safety guidelines to reduce the risk of injury.

Inexperienced coaches

The coach should have the appropriate qualifications for the level that they are coaching as well as regular continuous professional development (CPD) to keep up to date with the latest research on coaching practice. Many governing bodies have coaching schemes that are constantly reviewed so that coaching qualifications can be maintained at the highest and safest of standards.

LINK IT UP

The importance of warming-up is explained on pages 18–19.

ACTIVITY

Over the years, some rules and regulations have changed in sport to try to reduce sports-related injuries (see Did you know?).

Carry out research on the National Football League (otherwise known as American Football) which had a change to the rules of the sport in 2005 and 2009.

Explain how the rules of the sport were changed and the reasons why these changes were made in relation to reducing injuries in that sport.

CHECK MY LEARNING

For the following scenarios, describe the possible causes of injury with reasons for each suggested cause.

1. Dorothy is 60 years old and has a fractured wrist after falling while taken part in a HIIT training session.

2. Max has a tooth knocked out from taking part in basketball.

3. Debbie arrives late for her netball session and strains a muscle when playing a netball game.

Physiological management of common sports injuries

Physiological management of a common sports injury includes the immediate management of the injury, such as any medical treatment, and then, if necessary, longer-term treatment, for example seeing a physiotherapist for rehabilitation.

Seeking medical advice

When a person suffers from a sports injury it is important to seek medical advice. It may be necessary to call emergency services if the injury is severe and needs immediate professional attention. Most sport and activity providers, however, will have on-site qualified first aiders who are trained to deal with most basic injuries. But complex sports injuries will usually require further treatment. If the injured person does have a complex sports injury and is not admitted to hospital they will usually be referred to a doctor.

Once the injury has been treated, an injured person may be referred to a physiotherapist to help them to recover from their injury. The main aim of a physiotherapist is to help the injured person restore full function to the injured area. However, this can take some time if the injury has been severe, so a full rehabilitation programme may be required to support the person's recovery.

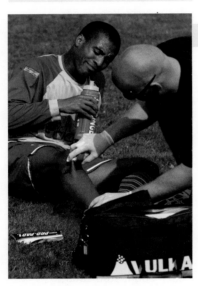

■ If injured when playing a sport, you should seek out a qualified first aider who can assist you.

SALTAPS

The sooner a person who has suffered a sports injury recognises it and has it treated appropriately, the sooner they will recover from the injury. The immediate treatment that a person who is helping to support an injured person can give can be summarised by the acronym SALTAPS:

Stop play.

Ask the casualty what is wrong and where they have pain.

Look for signs of bleeding, deformity of limbs, inflammation, swelling and redness.

Touch the injury or close to the injury for signs of heat, tenderness, loss or change of sensation and pain.

Active movement – ask the casualty to move the injured area. If they are able to move the injured area ask them to move it through its full range of movements.

Passive movement – try to move the injured site only if a good range of movement is available.

Strength – if the casualty has been taken through the steps above with no pain, use resisted movements to assess loss of function. An example of resisted movement for an injured ankle would involve helping the casualty to their feet, then asking them to stand unaided, then progressing the test to ask them to walk on the injured ankle and, if they can do this, then ask them to run on it.

The process of SALTAPS helps to determine the extent and severity of the injury, although it may be obvious. Treatment at this stage should consist of protect, rest, ice, compression, elevation (PRICE). For basic injuries, all stages of SALTAPS can usually be completed. But if a person sustains a complex sports injury, such as a fracture or dislocation, the assessment process should not be completed because further injury may occur.

In pairs, one person should pretend they have sustained a sports injury – choosing from a sprain, a strain, a ligament tear or a fracture. Review the symptoms of the selected injury from earlier in this book. The other person should then carry out SALTAPS to try and assess the type of injury, with the injured person talking through their symptoms. The aim of this activity is for the person treating the injury to work out what injury has been sustained and the severity of the injury.

PRICE

One of the responses a person feels when they are injured is pain due to the chemicals that are released from the damaged cells and the swelling of the injured area. The swelling creates pressure on the nerves surrounding the damaged tissue which causes this pain. Swelling around an injury occurs because the surrounding blood vessels are ruptured which allows blood to bleed into the injury site as well as tissue fluid. The injury site area will usually look red because the blood vessels surrounding the site will widen to increase blood flow to the area, which makes the area feel hot. The amount of swelling and pain is directly related to the severity of the injury.

The main concern therefore when treating an injury is to try to reduce the swelling of the injury site. This process is known as PRICE as this can help to limit the severity of the injury.

Protect the injured body part from further injury.

Rest – as soon as a person has injured themselves they should discontinue their sport or activity as further participation could cause further injury.

Ice – an ice pack or cold compress should be applied to the injured area. This will help to reduce the swelling as it reduces blood flow to the area; it will also help to reduce the pain of the injury.

Compression – gentle pressure should be applied to the injury site by surrounding the area with padding or a compressive bandage. Compressing the injured area will reduce blood flowing to the injury site and also help to control swelling by decreasing fluid seeping into the injured area from injured tissue cells.

Elevation – the injured area should be supported in a raised position above the level of the heart in order to reduce the blood flow to the injury, which will further help to minimise swelling and bruising at the injury site.

Recall each stage of SALTAPS in the correct order.

Explain why each stage of the SALTAPS process is in place and its importance when assessing a person with a sports injury.

Explain why ice, compression and elevation are used in the PRICE process.

You will need a bandage and a partner to carry out this activity. One person will be the patient, the other will be the first aider.

Attempt to wrap a bandage around an imaginary injured joint – either the ankle or the knee. Make sure the bandage provides sufficient compression to meet the requirements of PRICE but is not too tight to totally restrict blood flow to the area. Then position the injured area so it is elevated above the level of the heart. Once complete, swap over and have a go at bandaging a different imaginary injured joint and elevating the area in line with PRICE.

Psychological management of common sports injuries

The psychological response to injury varies from individual to individual but initially is nearly always negative as the person is unable to participate in sport or physical activity in the short term. The first reaction is usually shock followed by disbelief and denial as many people don't realise the significance of the injury and don't believe that it will cause too much of a problem. These initial responses are then often followed by possible further responses including anger directed towards themselves or towards other people and blaming themselves or others for doing something wrong which resulted in the injury.

It is therefore important to take into account and use psychological management of common sports injuries to help to support the person to recover from their injury.

Goal setting

Goal setting plays a key role in helping a person to recover from a sports injury and to support the rehabilitation process: it can increase the amount of effort an athlete puts into their rehabilitation programme. A goal is what a person is aiming to achieve. By setting a goal the person plans some key outcomes using steps they need to achieve in order to produce the key outcome.

Goal setting should follow the SMART principles. SMART stands for:

Specific – the goal has to state exactly what is needed; for example, 'After the rehabilitation programme my goal is to be able to sprint at the same speed as before I was injured'

Measurable – an ability to measure if the goal has been reached. In line with the example of a sprinting-specific goal, if the person already knows their sprint speed from measuring it over a specific distance, such as 100 m, they can then time their sprinting speed post injury and compare this to their speed before injury. They will then know when they have achieved their goal by comparing the pre-injury and post-injury sprint times over 100 m

Achievable – the goal has to be something that the athlete can do within the time frame given. For example, if a person fractured a bone in their leg it would not be achievable to have a goal to sprint at full speed if the time frame is only six weeks. However, if the time frame is six months then this goal would be achievable

Realistic – any barriers that the participant may face should be considered when setting a goal to ensure there is nothing that could prevent them from achieving the set goal.

Time-bound – a specific time frame needs to be given for completion of the set goal – this is usually set for at least a few weeks up to a number of months

Goal setting will usually include a number of goals to focus on, for example:
- a performance goal – this is a goal to achieve specific performance objectives which is not related to other sports-related abilities
- a process goal – this is where the person has to focus on what actions they must carry out in order to perform well. An example of this may be to do with putting in as much effort as possible during the rehabilitation sessions

- outcome goal – this is a goal that focuses on being able to perform a specific outcome; an example of this would be being able to spring and dribble a ball in basketball.

Goal setting techniques help the person recovering from the injury to see that they are progressing through the rehabilitation process in a positive way. It also helps the person to have realistic expectations about what they can hope to achieve during specific time frames.

Relaxation techniques

Relaxation techniques focus on relaxing tense muscles and are used to calm a person down. This process can help the injured person to deal with any negative feelings they may have about getting injured and/or the rehabilitation process if they are not recovering from the injury as quickly as they had hoped.

Progressive muscular relaxation (PMR) is a technique which involves tightening and relaxing the muscles in sequence.

ACTIVITY

Carry out your own PMR.

Find a comfortable place to lie down on your back. Close your eyes and deepen your breathing.

Now tense your hands by making a fist, hold for 10 seconds then relax.

Repeat this process working up through to your arms, then shoulders, to your face and then neck, then down your back and then bottom and then finish with your legs and then your feet.

Feel your body sinking into the floor as your whole body relaxes, and breathe deeply and calmly for five minutes, enjoying the feeling of being relaxed.

PMR helps a person to feel the difference between tensed and relaxed muscles. This then helps them to learn how to quickly relax muscles when feeling stressed and so helps them to feel calm. Another method of relaxation is breathing control. When a person is stressed they will usually be quite anxious and this produces short, shallow breathing. However, relaxation helps to deepen the breathing rate. The process essentially involves concentrating on breathing in and out and counting up to a certain number to control how long the breathing in and breathing out process lasts. This whole process helps to relax the body and mind.

◻ **Many yoga classes include a relaxation section at the end of the class which uses breathing control as a form of relaxation.**

CHECK MY LEARNING

Think about a sports injury you or someone you know has had (this could be a friend or a well-known sports performer). Go through the goal setting process to show how goal setting could be used to help the person recover from their injury. Ensure SMART principles are used and give examples for each SMART principle.

Basic rehabilitation from common sports injuries

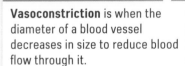

◻ Applying an ice pack can help to minimise swelling and bruising.

Rehabilitation from a sports injury is the process of restoring the injured area back to normal function. The time spent in rehabilitation varies depending upon the severity of the sports injury. A person with a minor sprained ankle, for example, will recover much more quickly than a person with a complete ligament tear in their ankle. It is very important for a person with a sports injury to listen to professional advice and take the required time to fully complete the rehabilitation programme.

Ice baths

Cooling an injured body part has a significant impact on minimising the swelling and bruising of an injured area and reducing the pain. The processes of injuring a body part means that blood vessels are torn and blood cells and fluid escape into the spaces among the muscle fibres. Placing the injured body part in an ice bath **vasoconstricts** the blood vessels in that area so blood flow to the area is reduced.

The cold water also reduces the release of chemicals that cause pain and inflammation as well as reducing the ability of the nerve endings which trigger feelings of pain.

Ice baths, where the injured area is immersed in cold water containing ice, should be used immediately after an injury has occurred. Depending upon how severe the injury is, their use should continue for usually at least two days, or up to three days, if the injury is more severe.

The cooling procedure should be repeated every two waking hours.

When using ice baths, the person will feel the following sensations of the area in the ice bath:
- cold
- burning
- aching
- numbness – as soon as the skin feels numb the person should remove their injured area from the ice bath.

Hot and cold treatment

This is also known as contrast bathing. This process uses alternating treatments of hot and cold therapy applied to the injury site. This part of the rehabilitation process should only be used when the swelling around the injury site has gone down. For most basic injuries, this is usually three days after the injury took place.

The hot treatment is usually carried out by placing the injured area in a hot water bath. This heat increases blood flow to the area. After some time, the hot water bath is replaced with a cold water bath which decreases blood flow to the area.

Heat pads and ice packs can also be used as other methods of heating and cooling the injured area rather than water baths. The increase in blood flow due to the heat has the effect of absorbing the swelling and removing the dead cells from the injury site. It will also help to increase the growth of new blood vessels in the area and help scar tissue to form.

The decrease in blood flow from the cold treatment means that the blood moves away from the injury site and takes with it the debris from the injury site. The injured site should be immersed in alternating hot and cold water for periods ranging from one to four minutes, with increased time initially in the cold water.

Basic strappings

Strapping is carried out to increase the stability of a joint when there has been an injury to the ligaments that normally support the joint. The strapping has the effect of limiting unwanted joint movement and supports the injured joint when taking part in rehabilitation exercises such as strengthening exercises by protecting the injury site from further damage.

Strapping uses adhesive tape or bandages to restrict the joint movement to within safe limits. It should not be carried out if the joint is still swollen or painful.

Flexibility exercises and yoga/Pilates

Rehabilitation from a sports injury will often involve exercises to increase the flexibility of the person and the injured area. This is because when a person has reduced flexibility, the range of movement in their joints can be reduced. This means they are more likely to injure the muscles, tendons or ligaments around the joint when taking part in sport or exercise. However, taking part in stretching exercises, which is included in exercise classes such as yoga and Pilates, will help to increase flexibility in areas of the body that have reduced movement. Pilates also focuses on strengthening the core muscles, which help to maintain a good posture (essential in helping to avoid injury).

◨ **Strapping around a joint can increase its stability, helping its rehabilitation after an injury such as a sprained ankle.**

◨ **Taking part in regular stretching sessions such as yoga can improve flexibility.**

CHECK MY LEARNING

Explain how using ice baths helps to reduce swelling at an injury site.

Explain how heat and ice treatment helps to remove debris from an injury.

Explain how strapping would help to support a person with a sprained wrist joint.

Use of technology in rehabilitation from common sports injuries

Technology can be used in rehabilitation from basic and complex injuries. However, as complex injuries usually take longer to heal compared with basic injuries, technology is more widely used to treat complex injuries. Elite sports performers, however, such as Premier League football players, may well have technology incorporated into their rehabilitation programmes for basic sports injuries to help to increase the speed of recovery so that they can return to play as soon as possible.

Cryotherapy chambers

Cryotherapy is the use of extreme cold as a form of treatment. We have already seen how using ice baths can be used as a basic form of rehabilitation and this is a type of cryotherapy. A cryotherapy chamber is a more extreme version of this.

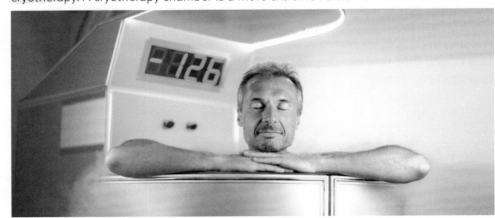

◻ **A cryotherapy chamber provides cold treatment to the whole body.**

A cryotherapy chamber provides cold treatment to the whole body. The person spends a short period of time, usually only a matter of a few minutes, in the chamber. The temperature of cryotherapy chambers varies but can be as low as −135°C. Research suggests that using cryotherapy chambers can be beneficial to all people who take part in sport and activity at a high level: it helps the body recover as it can help reduce feelings of pain and inflammation. Research is ongoing to confirm other benefits of using cryotherapy chambers to support rehabilitation from sports injuries.

Hyperbaric oxygen treatment

Hyperbaric oxygen treatment means a person is given higher levels of oxygen compared to the amount of oxygen they would normally breathe in when not using this treatment.

In a hyperbaric chamber the oxygen pressure is above atmospheric pressure (this is what hyperbaric means). Some researchers have suggested this type of treatment can help in the rehabilitation of sports injuries by reducing the recovery time. This is because oxygen is essential to the tissues in the body and any tissues that are damaged will require extra oxygen to help them to heal. Hyperbaric oxygen treatment increases the supply of oxygen to injured areas. The amount of time and number of sessions a person should use a hyperbaric oxygen chamber for varies.

◻ **A hyperbaric oxygen chamber can help in recovery by increasing the amount of oxygen to damaged tissue.**

Resistance bands

Resistance bands are essentially similar to large elastic bands, made from very tough elastic. They are used as a form of exercise to help to rehabilitate the injured area by increasing the strength of the area. How easily these bands can be stretched varies from band to band, which offers a range of different amounts of resistance.

A person rehabilitating from a sports injury can use these to provide a force to push or pull against with the injured area. As the person increases their strength, bands with higher resistance can be used which helps to provide gradual increases in the intensity of the exercise. This helps to ensure the person does not use too high a resistance in the initial stages of rehabilitation, as stressing the recovering area too much could lead to further injury.

◘ Resistance bands are an effective and simple way to help increase strength to injured areas.

ACTIVITY

You will need a resistance band for this activity.

Using a resistance band, work out different exercises that can be used as strengthening exercises for the following body areas:

knee   wrist   elbow   shoulder

Draw stick diagrams of the exercise to show how the band is used to provide resistance for each body part.

Electronic pulse massage systems

Electronic pulse massages work by using small electric impulses fired directly over the injured area which stimulates the muscle tissue. This helps to reduce pain and inflammation, assisting the tissue to heal more quickly and repair the injury. The pulse massage system also stimulates the nerves around the sports injury area which helps to reduce the sensation of pain felt in the injury site. Research suggests that this form of rehabilitation does help to increase the speed of recovery from some sports injuries.

CHECK MY LEARNING

Explain why it is only possible to use cryotherapy chambers for very short periods of time.

Describe what is meant by hyperbaric oxygen treatment.

Explain how an electronic pulse massage system works.

Learning aim B: assessment practice

How you will be assessed

For this part of the component you will need to explore one basic and one complex sporting injury, including the symptoms and causes of each and the different ways to manage injuries. You will also need to create a rehabilitation plan to aid recovery.

CHECKPOINT

Strengthen

- Explain one basic and one complex sporting injury, giving sport-related examples of how each may occur.
- Describe the symptoms of one basic and one complex sporting injury.
- Explain how you would manage each sporting injury.
- Create a rehabilitation plan for each sporting injury.

Challenge

- Explain how technology can be used in the rehabilitation plan for each sporting injury.
- Give justified reasons for the management and rehabilitation process for each sporting injury.

ASSESSMENT ACTIVITY   LEARNING AIM   B

With a partner, one person simulates having a sports injury, choosing from an injury in either the basic or complex category of sports injuries.

Basic sports injury	Complex sports injury
Sprain	Dislocation
Strain	Ligament tear
Bruise	Fracture
	Tendonitis
	Shin splints

The partner with the injury should ensure they are fully aware of the symptoms of the injury.

The other person is then responsible for diagnosing the injury based on asking questions about how the injury occurred, how the person is feeling and the symptoms presented by the 'injured' person.

The person diagnosing the injury should do the following:

Identify the injury.

Explain the possible causes of the injury.

Carry out initial management of the injury explaining what they are doing and why they are doing it.

Explain to the injured person basic rehabilitation for that injury.

Explain to the injured person how technology could be used in the rehabilitation of the injury.

Once this is complete, swap over with the person who is injured and select a different injury from a different category.

TIPS

You may be able to use bandages and ice packs if they are available at your school. This will help you to fully understand and carry out the processes required to manage common sporting injuries.

TAKE IT FURTHER

For the injury you treated and the injury that you selected, explain ways these injuries could be prevented.

Different types of technology in sport and activity – equipment

Advances in equipment

The equipment used to take part in sport and activity has advanced over the years. Equipment includes what the person uses to play the game, such as a tennis racket, and also includes the apparatus used to score goals, such as basketball nets and backboards, goal posts, etc. In addition, any equipment used by a sports person for strengthening and conditioning is included in the term 'equipment'.

Advances in equipment can impact a participant's experience in an activity or sport, by improving performance and helping to prevent injury.

Tennis rackets

Tennis and badminton have changed a lot over the years, partly due to advances in science and technology. Tennis players are hitting the ball harder and faster than ever before. In badminton, the rackets are much lighter and more aerodynamic which allows the player to hit the ball with more power.

The design of a racket is very important and it should allow a player to give their best performance, for example by allowing them to serve the ball as fast as possible.

As Table 1.2 shows, racket design has developed over the years to increase performance as well as reduce overuse injuries.

◻ **Table 1.2 The design of rackets has changed over the years**

Part of the racket	Older tennis rackets	New tennis rackets	Benefit of new technology
Frame	Wood	**Metal composite**	Lighter racket requires less energy for player to move it More flexible to help absorb impact from the ball as it is hit which helps to reduce overuse injuries
Head	Small head	Larger head	Greater power can be produced and larger **'sweet spot'**
Shaft	Wood	Metal composite	More flexible to absorb the impact from hitting the ball and less flexible so more power can be generated when hitting the ball
Grip	Leather	Artificial fabrics	Helps to increase grip on the racket and improve performance
Strings	Made from animal guts	Artificial filaments used to make strings	The new strings absorb the impact of hitting the ball at great speed to prevent overuse injuries; are able to help the player hit the ball with more power; and the strings are able to withstand high forces to last a long time The strings are also more ethically sourced as they are no longer from animal sources

◘ Wooden tennis rackets were used until around 1968.

◘ Tennis rackets began to be made out of a metal composite in the 1980s.

Footballs

These have also developed over the years. The first footballs were made from animal bladders. These balls were blown up by mouth and then knotted to seal the air in the bladder. They were then made from leather but these absorbed water and would get much heavier if the game was played in wet conditions. Later a type of rubber was used to make the ball, also requiring a pump to blow it up but which did result in the ball being spherical. Now there are set guidelines for the circumference, weight and inflation pressure for a football used in FIFA competitive games.

The material used to cover footballs has been developed to help ensure it doesn't deform during a game and also to ensure the stitching or covering does not create ways to kick the ball that can add in additional swerve or spin.

Footballs are being developed now that have goal-line technology. This helps referees make their decisions as to whether a goal has been scored as it provides feedback to a computer to track its location. Therefore it can show if the ball did cross the goal line or not.

Goalposts

Goalposts have also changed over the years. Initially a football goal had to have two goalposts set at 24 feet apart but no specific height was set. A goal could be scored at any height, the ball just had to pass within the two goal posts. Then tape was placed at a height of 8 feet across both goalposts to indicate the height in which the ball had to pass between them for a goal to be scored. A crossbar soon became compulsory. Nets were then introduced. Goalposts are now made from light but strong metal and are a rounded shape rather than square to help to prevent injury if a player were to fall into the goalpost.

Strengthening equipment

To help a person to increase their strength, weights used to be the only real option, in the form of barbells and dumbbells. Now there is a huge range of strengthening equipment including resistance machines, kettle bells and isokinetic machines, which means the person using the equipment experiences the same amount of force at any point when lifting the weights.

ACTIVITY

Carry out research to find out about other sports that use goalposts.

List sports that use just two goalposts with no crossbar.

List sports that use goalposts and a crossbar.

Explain the advantages and disadvantages of having a crossbar in a football goal.

CHECK MY LEARNING

For a sport of your choice, carry out research to find out how the equipment used in that sport has changed over the years and how it has helped to improve performance in that specific sport.

Use the same layout as Table 1.2, the tennis racket comparison table, to help you to write up your research.

Different types of technology in sport and activity – protection

Identify what protective equipment the ice hockey goal keeper is wearing, the areas of the body that it is protecting and explain why the ice hockey player is wearing that protection.

Advances in protection

As we know, participation in sport and activity can occasionally result in participants getting injured. Taking part in certain sports and activities can mean a participant is at a greater risk of injury because of the equipment used to play the sport or the types of activities included in the sport. As a result, advances in protective equipment are continually taking place to help to reduce the risk of injury.

Cricket helmets

These have developed over the last few years but only became commonplace for cricketers to wear when batting in the 1970s. The main concern in cricket is to protect the person from being hit by the ball. If a cricket ball were to hit a person's head it can cause serious injury or even death – therefore, helmets are worn to try and protect the head from injury. These helmets are made of very strong but light materials to protect the head and now include a face guard to protect the face.

◘ Cricket helmets have advanced over the years to now include a face guard to protect the face.

Mouth guards

Dental injuries can occur from taking part in some sports and research suggests they are in fact the most common type of facial injury in sports. Mouth guards can help to prevent teeth from being knocked out and also help to protect the jaw. The materials used to make mouth guards are now thin, flexible pieces of plastic that are placed in the mouth and over the teeth to protect them during any sports activity.

The main cost associated with buying mouth guards is how well the mouth guard will fit. Cheaper guards use a 'boil-and-bite' option where the mouth guard is heated in hot water to make it softer and then placed in the person's mouth to mould around the teeth. When it cools down it keeps this shape. Custom-made mouth guards are also available which are made by a dentist or orthodontist; these are considered to be the most comfortable as well as the most protective option.

Landing mats

In sports such as gymnastics, landing mats are essential to help cushion the impact of landing from a tumble or vault, for example. The technology of the foam used inside landing mats has improved over the years so that they can absorb the shock of the landing impact to a much higher degree. The materials used on the surface of the mats have also been developed to provide greater stability and support to the person landing.

Both of these developments help to reduce the risk of injuries associated with a single landing, such as a dislocation, or repeated landings, such as a stress fracture.

◻ Landing mats provide cushioning to the impact of landing in sports.

Different types of technology in sport and activity – clothing

Clothing

The clothing that people now have available has developed considerably over the years. When you consider the clothing worn in 1953 by Edmund Hillary, who was the first person to scale Everest, and compare it with the clothing climbers are wearing today, there are clear differences in the materials used.

◘ What differences can you see in the materials worn by mountaineers such as Sir Edmund Hillary in the 1950s to those worn by climbers today?

ACTIVITY

Carry out research to find out what materials were used to make the clothing worn by Edmund Hillary when he first climbed Everest.

Carry out more research to discover how clothing has developed over the years to make it better for climbers in very cold conditions.

Aerodynamic clothing

Aerodynamic clothing means it reduces the forces of air moving past it. When a person or object moves through air, drag forces are created which act to resist the movement. The faster a person or object travels, the greater the drag forces are that act upon them. Therefore, sports such as cycling where the person travels very fast are more greatly affected by drag in comparison to events such as long-distance running where a person is not travelling as fast. Clothing that is not fitted tightly to the body can create extra drag force from air resistance. Therefore, clothing that is aerodynamic can help to reduce the air resistance for a person when they are moving.

◘ Cyclists wear tight fitting clothing to help make them more aerodynamic.

Compression clothing

Compression clothing is relatively new and it is worn so that it fits tightly around the skin. The benefits are that it helps to increase blood flow to the area covered by this clothing and this helps to improve performance and recovery time. This is because blood brings oxygen and nutrients to working muscles and also removes waste products. Therefore, having more blood flow to the area is going to help to increase the delivery of oxygen and nutrients for the muscles to use when exercising. More blood flow also increases the removal of the waste products such as carbon dioxide and lactic acid which are produced by the working muscles.

Many people who take part in non-competitive sports and activities, such as fun runners, wear compression clothing as they believe it helps to improve their running performance and recovery.

☐ Athletes used to wear much looser clothing, which would have been less aerodynamic compared with what athletes wear today.

ACTIVITY

Carry out research to find out about compression clothing.

Describe three different types of compression clothing.

Identify where they are worn.

Identify which muscles are being targeted by the clothing.

Explain what types of sport or activity may benefit from wearing these types of compression clothing.

Moisture control

When taking part in sport or activity, a person will get hotter because exercising muscles produces heat. The body tries to cool itself down by sweating – the harder a person exercises the more they will sweat which will make their clothing wet. Clothing that absorbs the sweat can become heavy and cling to the person. However, new clothing fabrics have been developed that have sweat-wicking properties. This means the fabric draws moisture away from the body and absorbs small amounts of the sweat which helps the person to stay cool and dry.

LINK IT UP

Remember, the body controls its temperature through vasodilation and vasoconstriction. More information about this can be found on page 7.

Perceived psychological edge

How a person feels when taking part in sport or activity can have a significant impact on their performance. If they feel they are wearing clothing that is going to benefit or improve their performance this can actually help them to perform better, even if the clothing does not provide any real impact on their actual performance.

As an example, a person who enjoys recreational cycling may buy a full set of specialist cycling clothing that is worn by their favourite Tour de France cycling team such as Team Sky. This may make them feel they look like a professional cyclist and help them to cycle further or faster than if they weren't wearing this clothing. This is because the power of the mind can really affect performance and many elite sports people will have a sports psychologist to advise them and help them to mentally prepare for their events.

CHECK MY LEARNING

Select one of the following sports: cycling, hiking or hockey.

Explain the types of clothing that are worn for participation in that sport to help to protect that person from injury.

Different types of technology in sport and activity – footwear

Footwear

Footwear is essential for participation in most sports and activities. Footwear is designed so that it is appropriate for the surface that the activity or sport is to be played on. There is a huge range of specialised footwear for all sports and activities, including running, basketball, rock climbing, tennis, squash, gymnastics, football, hiking and rugby. All these specialised pieces of footwear are made to be supportive to the participant and totally suitable for the surface required for the sport or activity. Football has grass, artificial turf and sports hall floors as its main playing areas and there are specialised boots for each surface.

Studs

Studs on footwear used for sports such as football or hockey have improved over time. In the past, although the studs helped the person wearing them to grip the playing surface, they could cause contact injuries to other players, for example in a tackle. Studs were made of metal but this has now been replaced with plastic. Plastic causes less damage if it makes contact with another player's body part.

New forms of studs have also been developed in the form of blades. These are larger than studs and therefore provide increased points of contact with the ground, which can increase the grip on the playing surface. When playing on hard ground, some participants find them more comfortable than studs. This is because the increased surface area in contact with the ground helps to spread the weight of the participant more evenly when they are running.

◘ Studs help the wearer to grip the playing surface but if made of metal they can cause contact injuries.

◘ **Blades are a new development in studs, which can spread the player's weight more evenly on the playing surface.**

Insoles

Insoles can be placed inside the footwear to offer specialised support for that person. For example, a marathon runner needs a lot of cushioning in their trainers to absorb the repeated impact of running. They can buy specialised running shoes and in addition also use insoles to increase the cushioning.

Insoles can also be used to provide correction for any concerns about a person's **gait**. The choice of footwear can have an impact on a person's gait as the footwear can control how the foot lands on the ground. This affects how the rest of the body reacts to the way the foot is placed on the ground.

Breathable and waterproof materials

In the past, most footwear was made of leather which was strong and long-lasting but was not breathable or waterproof. Today, sports footwear is mainly made out of synthetic fibres. These fibres are strong but very light which is important if the footwear needs to provide protection to the person's foot and ankle area.

Breathable materials help sweat to evaporate and keep the foot dry and cool. Waterproof material helps to keep the foot dry even in wet weather conditions. This helps to keep the skin around the foot healthy as well as preventing rubbing which may cause blisters.

KEY TERM

Gait means how a person walks, jogs or runs.

ACTIVITY

Carry out research to find out about footwear for a sport of your choice. Select three types of footwear for your chosen sport and explain how the materials used help to reduce the risk of injury to yourself and other participants.

CHECK MY LEARNING

Select one of the following sports: cycling, hiking or hockey.

Explain the footwear that should be worn to help to protect the participant from injury.

Different types of technology in sport and activity – computer-based technology

Discuss with a partner the different types of computer technology that you use or know of that is used for a sport of your choice. You could consider technology that can be used on mobile phones for example or technology that you have seen from game analysis when watching sport on TV. Explain how you think this technology may help to improve the performance of participants taking part in your selected sport.

Computer-based technology

This type of technology includes cameras, computers and software. As computers improve in terms of their design and function, they can be used to greater degrees within sport and activity. They are usually used to either help officials to make decisions and confirm if a player is meeting the rules of the sport, or to help to improve participant performance.

Hawk-Eye™

This is technology used to track the ball in a sport and provide a profile of the path the ball took at any point during the game. This helps in games such as tennis to determine if the ball bounces out of the play area when serving or during play. It is used in other sports such as volleyball, rugby, football and cricket, again to determine the location of the ball at crucial moments when it is not clear from looking at the ball during live play.

Goal-line technology

This has been introduced in football to determine if the football has crossed the goal line during a game. The technology uses high speed cameras located around the football pitch which are directed at both goals. The officials can use this device to support the decision-making process. The technology was approved in 2012 and is used in high-level competitions.

Match analysis

During and after a competitive game, match analysis is carried out by experienced professionals. They analyse the home team players' and the opponents' positions during the game and performance in order to work out tactics to help them to gain an advantage. You may have seen this in action when watching sports programmes such as a premier league football match where the commentators provide some analysis of key performers in the game. The technology uses video analysis software tools to allow this match analysis to take place.

Participant player analysis

To help a participant and their coach or manager gain a better understanding of their performance, participant player analysis can be carried out using various types of technology. Video software focuses on the individual, and tracks their skills and techniques and responses to opponents throughout the course of a game. This can then be played back and key strengths can be noted. For example, in hockey the ability to sprint quickly and intercept a ball can be noted as well as any areas for improvement such as the technique for dribbling the ball.

Action camera

An action camera is a digital camera that can be worn by the participant when they are taking part in a sport or activity. They are usually waterproof and can withstand some impact. They can be attached to the person using a chest harness or worn on clothing, helmets and cycling handlebars.

◻ **An action camera can be worn by one participant to film another so their performance or activity can be analysed afterwards.**

An action camera provides footage of what the person sees when they are taking part in a sport or activity. It can be used by a coach to record footage of an individual when they are taking part in their sport. The footage can then be analysed in relation to the performer's skills and techniques to see if there are areas to improve upon.

GPS

This stands for Global Positioning System, which uses satellites to track the location of the person or object using the GPS device. GPS is used on a variety of fitness tracking devices such as an Apple™ watch or Fitbit™; it has also been integrated into sports clothing. This device helps the performer to track how fast they have travelled and how far they have travelled over different parts of their sport or activity. The device will also usually be linked with a heart rate tracker.

Smartwatches

Many different types of smartwatches are available today and while they do tell the time, most will also provide key data such as heart rate, distance travelled, number of steps taken and speed. Some smartwatches can be worn when swimming which help to track physiological variables when in water, but not all smartwatches are waterproof. These devices are small so are easily worn as part of everyday attire and don't affect performance.

Apps

An app is an application that is a type of computer program. There is a huge range of apps available and they are constantly being developed and refined. Many different apps are available to track key physiological data such as heart rate. They can also track the distance a person has travelled and the speed at which they travelled. This helps a person to work out if there are any components of fitness that they should train to improve. They can also record progress if the activity is part of a training programme.

ACTIVITY

A lot of sports do not allow a person to wear jewellery or watches, as these could catch on other people or equipment and cause injury to the person wearing the watch or another participant. This means smartwatches cannot be worn by participants taking part in lots of different sports such as basketball or rugby.

Think about the kinds of devices (that are available now, or which could be invented) that could track physiological data in the same way as a smartwatch but which could be worn by participants who are not permitted to wear watches when taking part in sport. Explain the devices, where they are worn and what sort of data could be collected by them.

CHECK MY LEARNING

For a sport or activity of your choice, explain how computer-based technology has developed and the impact it has had on participation in your selected sport or activity.

Different types of technology in sport and activity – facilities

The facilities are the areas in which the sport or activity is carried out. Facilities have developed over the years to help participants feel more comfortable when taking part in sport or activity, as well as to increase safety and improve performance.

Climate control

The climate in which the sport is taking place must be appropriate for the activity. Facilities such as an ice rink for skating or ice hockey would have different considerations than, for example, a studio for gymnastics regarding the maintenance of temperature.

As taking part in sport and activity generally increases body temperature, air conditioning in an indoor facility is very important to help a person to maintain their body temperature. If the facility did not have air conditioning, in hot weather the participants could get extremely hot which increases the rate at which they would fatigue. This could make them stop their activity sooner than if they were in cooler conditions. Air conditioning can also increase the temperature in the facility which again is useful if the weather outside is cold. Cold conditions mean that muscle temperature is low and this can lead to a greater increase of muscle strain as muscles are less pliable when they are cold.

Air management is the process of increasing air quality, which is a concern if the air around the facility has the potential to be polluted. Pollution of the air can be harmful to health and comes from a variety of sources including vehicle emissions. A gym that is located next to a busy road may install air management mechanisms to increase the quality of the air that the people are breathing in when exercising at the gym.

Indoor flooring

Sprung floors

These have been developed to help to absorb some of the impact experienced from **high impact** sports and activities. Many exercise studios which hold classes such as circuit training or HIIT training classes have wooden sprung floors.

Wooden floors

Many gyms have wooden floors as this is the preferred surface for some sports such as basketball. This is because the type of wood used is durable and also helps to absorb shock. This is beneficial to participants using the floor as it helps to reduce the risk of injuries such as overuse injuries like shin splints. However, it does cost quite a lot to maintain.

Rubber flooring

This type of flooring is often used in weight rooms in a gym or fitness centre. It helps to absorb shock from weights being placed back on the ground, has anti-slip properties and is water resistant, which is useful if participants spill their drinks while using the gym equipment.

Outdoor flooring

In the past, outdoor flooring essentially used to consist of grass for playing sports such as rugby and hockey, or other surfaces such as clay for sports such as tennis. However, with grass and clay, rain can affect the surface by making it slippery or unsuitable to use, for instance when a pitch is waterlogged or when it is frozen and too hard to play on. Now outdoor flooring is available that allows participants to use it in all weathers. These are artificial surfaces and have different names to reflect the different types of materials used to make the surface.

CHECK MY LEARNING

For an indoor and outdoor sport or activity of your choice, explain what facilities are used for participation in each sport. Explain ways in which technology has developed to make the facilities more comfortable for participants as well as improve their performance.

The benefits of technology for the performer

World records in sport and activities are continuing to be broken as athletes improve their abilities. These improvements are partly due to a range of technological advancements that help an athlete to improve their preparation for an event through training and also to improve their performance during an event.

Marginal gains

Marginal gains refers to the improvement in every small aspect of a competitor's experience, with the intention of making gains in their performance. This could include nutrition, equipment, clothing, methods to maximise sleep, post-race recovery methods, etc.

This concept was followed very closely by Sir David Brailsford, the Tour de France Team Sky coach. He looked for small improvements that could be made in any area that the Tour de France rider was going to experience over the 23-day racing period. This methodology is thought to have had a significant positive impact on Team Sky's performance as the team had the first British rider to ever win the Tour De France in 2012.

Marginal gains in body systems

Using equipment to analyse a performer's skill can lead to marginal gains in the body systems of sports performers, such as the musculoskeletal system. Equipment and technology can be used to track the performer as they compete or train. This can then provide physiological data such as their heart rate, power output, distance they have travelled, overall speed, and speed at various points in the race or game, etc. Analysis will present data on the fitness of the sports performer and highlight any areas that would benefit from improvement in order to help their performance of the various skills required for their event.

This will then usually mean fitness training programmes tailored to the specific needs of that performer to improve their musculoskeletal system, as well as their cardiorespiratory system. This helps to increase their performance.

Clothing

Specialist clothing has been developed to help to make the performer more aerodynamic by reducing the amount of drag experienced by the performer. Air resistance is where air pushes on a moving object, slowing it down. The larger the area coming into contact with the air, the larger the resistance – this is called drag. The more drag a performer experiences, the harder that person has to work in order to move forwards. In sports where the performer is travelling at speed, such as in cycling, drag can have a significant impact on how fast a person travels and therefore how hard they have to work to cycle at speed.

ACTIVITY

To show how air resistance and drag affects the speed of moving objects, carry out the following activity.

Get two pieces of A4 paper. Crumple one of the pieces of paper into a ball.

Now hold the flat piece of A4 paper and the crumpled-up piece of paper in one hand each. Drop the two pieces of paper at exactly the same time.

Which piece of paper hits the floor first?

Explain why you think which paper hit the floor first in relation to air resistance.

■ Prosthetics have been developed for specialist use in sports, such as the blades worn by Paralympic runners.

GPS

GPS devices allow the performer to monitor their cardiorespiratory training zones. Technology can show if they are training at the right level of intensity in order to train either their aerobic or anaerobic systems. It will also show if they are pushing their cardiorespiratory system to maximal capacity when competing or if they could put in more effort during the event.

Use of prosthetics

These are artificial devices that are used to replace a missing body part. In sport and activity, specific prosthetics can be used with the musculoskeletal system. Technology has developed to support people with missing lower limbs to compete in events such as running races. The prosthetics are now developed so that they are much more advanced, such as the blades worn by Paralympic runners which are specifically designed for sprinting.

Supination

Footwear

This has been improved over the years to suit the biomedical needs of the performer. The footwear a person chooses can have a significant impact on reducing the risk of a person getting injured due to the structural abnormalities in their body.

Insoles have been developed which can be fitted to a person to correct a biomechanical alignment concern or correct a structural abnormality. They are designed to meet the person's specific needs and custom-made for that person. They will then wear these insoles in their footwear to correct the area of concern. They can usually be worn in most footwear and used for walking, running and playing sport.

Pronation

■ Figure 1.12: Supination is where the foot rolls outwards, and pronation is where the foot rolls inwards

Many people have a specific biomedical need because their feet either pronate or supinate.

Pronation is where the foot rolls inwards due to some collapse in the arch on the inside. There may be some pronation in a person's foot; however, too much pronation can lead to injuries. Supination is where the foot rolls outwards due to some collapse in the arch of the foot to the outside. There may be some supination in a person's foot; however, too much supination can lead to injuries.

If the person has overpronation or oversupination, most trainers these days will be able to provide some support and help to balance the inward or outward roll of the foot. This can be done either by the trainer alone or with the lining inside the trainer.

CHECK MY LEARNING

For a sport of your choice, explain ways in which technology has impacted on the body systems to improve performance, including musculoskeletal improvements, the use of clothing, footwear, GPS and prosthetics.

The benefits of technology for the coach/manager and officials

GETTING STARTED

Select three sports. For each sport, describe how a team or individual can score points. Explain if the method of scoring points can sometimes not be seen by an official, or if other parts of the game can sometimes be missed by an official but can have a significant impact on the outcome of the game. Describe how technology could be used to support an official to make decisions in each of your selected sports.

The coach/manager

The coach is the person who is ultimately responsible for the training of the performer or team. How elite the team or performer is will determine how many people are actually involved in that person's training. For relatively low-level clubs such as a school basketball team, there will usually only be one coach. However, for a basketball team that is part of the NBA in America, there will be a huge range of coaches specialising in training the players for specific techniques and tactics. There will also be coaches who are only concerned with training specific components of fitness. These are usually referred to as strength and conditioning coaches. In these cases, there will then be a head coach who is in charge of all the other coaches.

The manager is usually the person who is in charge of the whole organisation, such as a football manager.

There is a huge variety of technology which can help the coach and manager to observe and monitor the performance of their performers. It can be used to help the performer to improve and also to determine if the coach/manager are going to keep coaching or managing that person.

Video analysis

This is where the player is observed from playing back footage of training or in competition to monitor how they performed and to spot areas for development.

Video analysis allows the observer to replay the movement of interest in slow motion and carry out analyses to gain in-depth information about how the performer executes a particular skill or technique. For example, when a javelin thrower throws the javelin the process is very fast and it is difficult to carry out a full analysis of the process. However, with video analysis, the movement can be played very slowly and 'stills' can be taken. Key information can therefore be recorded, such as the angle that the javelin was released, the angle and location of other body parts, etc. This can then inform the performer how they can adapt their throw in order to maximise performance.

Cardiorespiratory effort can also be assessed using video analysis to calculate the speed of the performer or the distance that they have covered in an event, used in conjunction with a heart rate monitor. This will then show the coach or manager the intensity that the performer was working at during these periods. They can then determine if they were working at their maximal intensity or if they have scope to work harder and therefore perform at a higher level.

■ A video of this sportsman's training is being analysed to gain in-depth information.

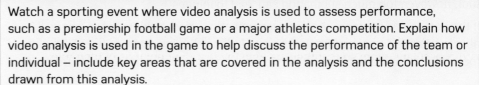

ACTIVITY

Watch a sporting event where video analysis is used to assess performance, such as a premiership football game or a major athletics competition. Explain how video analysis is used in the game to help discuss the performance of the team or individual – include key areas that are covered in the analysis and the conclusions drawn from this analysis.

GPS technology

GPS is used to track the location of the performer at various points in training and competition, to provide data on factors such as distance covered and speed. From this the cardiorespiratory effort can be assessed if the heart rate is also captured. This will allow coaches and managers to select their squad based on the cardiorespiratory capacity of their performers. For example in football, those with high aerobic capacity often make good defenders as they need to be able to keep running back to their side of the pitch to defend the goal throughout the 90-minute game (or even longer if the game goes to extra time).

Use of apps

An app is an application that is a type of computer program. There is a huge range of apps available and they are constantly being developed and refined. They can be used for many different purposes to help coaches and managers track the physiological progress as well as the psychological progress of their sports performers. For example, apps are available that can help to rate the mood of the performer. This helps the coach or manager to determine if psychological intervention would be beneficial for the performer. For example, if the person gets so nervous before a competition that it stops them sleeping, then a sports psychologist and relaxation techniques will help them to cope with these nerves.

ACTIVITY

Carry out research to find out about at least one type of app that is used to analyse sports performance. Explain the features of the app and how information gained from the app would help to provide useful information about an individual's sporting performance.

The officials

A person who has the role of an official is responsible for upholding the rules of the sport or activity and ensuring all participants are following the rules appropriately and playing the sport in a safe and fair manner. It is important that they are able to fully focus on the game or event that they are officiating and have as little as possible to distract them. For many sports an official will need to be close to the play and therefore will need to be fit so that they are always able to run to have good vision of play.

In football it is estimated that a referee runs up to 12 miles during a game – which is 5 more miles than most players! Technology to help the referee to cope with the demands of exercising is therefore going to be beneficial to them.

Moisture control clothing

Clothing that absorbs sweat can become heavy and cling to the person. However, new clothing fabrics have been developed that have sweat-wicking properties. Officials should make use of this type of clothing so they can follow players to observe play.

Use of smartwatches

Officials can use smartwatches to track heart rate as well as distance covered and speed. This will help them to analyse the cardiovascular demands of their role. If they find they are having difficulty keeping up with play, and their smartwatch data shows their cardiovascular system is working to maximal capacity, the official could decide they need to take part in fitness training. This will help them to develop their cardiovascular system so that they are able to meet the demands of their role.

CHECK MY LEARNING

Imagine you are the coach or manager for a selected sports person or team of your choice. Explain how using technology would help you to assess the performance of the participants and to select participants for competition.

Limitations of technology to sport and activity for the performer

GETTING STARTED

As a sports performer there are several advantages to technology and it can have a positive impact on sporting performance. However, consider how technology may have a negative effect on the sports performer. With a partner, discuss ways in which technology has not been beneficial for your participation or performance in a sport and/or activity.

While technology has provided huge advances in sports performance, it can also have a negative effect on the performance or playing opportunities for some participants.

Data from technology

◘ **Data can be collected from technology, such as a GPS data vest, worn by the participant.**

Data collected from technology such as GPS vests, which track a player's location to provide information on the distance they have covered and their speed, can show that the player does not have the fitness or ability to play at a certain level or in a specific position. This can be disappointing for the performer who may have always had their sights set on playing in a certain position such as a wing in rugby. However, the data collected by technology showing where the player was usually positioned during the game and if they struggled to keep up with play due to concerns with fitness levels may suggest to the manager or coach that the position a performer is playing in is not appropriate for their skill set.

Data from technology is also used to compare performers. Two or more players may hope to be selected to play for a specific competition in a certain position but the person with the best data printout is selected.

The use of technology in these situations provides physiological data, but this may not always be the best way to determine how a player will perform in a competitive situation. The skill set and mental state of the performer are also very important. This means a player may be selected because of the physiological data, as they have demonstrated they have the higher fitness levels and can run more quickly. However, if they are very anxious in a game or become aggressive in competitive situations then this will negatively affect their performance and mean they may not be the better player to select for the event.

Data and injury assessment

When a participant is going through rehabilitation to recover from an injury, data is usually collected to track their progress. This is used to determine when they are fit enough to return to their selected sport or activity. If the participant is very keen to return and the data suggests they are not fully fit, this can be very disappointing and potentially have a negative impact on their rehabilitation programme. This is because they may feel the programme is not working and therefore do not put as much effort in as they did before.

They may also benefit from participating in only part of the game, for example being substituted in for the last 10 minutes of play, to help them build up their confidence, ready to play a full game. However, the data from the injury assessment may state that the player should not participate at all.

DID YOU KNOW?

In sports such as basketball, where the substitution rules allow for an individual player to be rotated on and off court throughout the entire length of the match, players returning from injury, particularly a major injury, are usually put on a 'minute's restriction'. A minute's restriction is when a basketball player returns to play games after an injury and is given a set number of minutes that they are able to play for. The number of minutes is enforced by the officials so the player is not able to play for longer than permitted, even if they want to or the team manager wants them to continue playing for longer. This enables the return from recovery to be monitored and controlled.

ACTIVITY

Think about how you have felt when you have returned to sport after recovering from a sports injury. Or consider a well-known sports performer that you have seen in the media who has returned to sport after having sustained an injury that meant they could not play for a period of time. Describe the process of how you or the sports performer returned to play. Did you/they play full games or compete in high-profile competitions straight away or was there a gradual return to sport?

CHECK MY LEARNING

Explain how technology can have the following limitations for a sports performer:
- impact their selection for sport or activity
- compare their performance to that of other participants
- impact their return to sport following an injury.

Limitations of technology to sport and activity for the coach/manager and officials

The coach/manager

Technology is very beneficial for the coach and manager to let them know how well the participants are doing and if they are putting in enough effort when training and competing. This will help them to determine which players to select for specific events and if they should continue to keep a participant in the team. However, there are several limitations to technology that should be considered by the coach and manager when they are thinking about investing in and using technology to help them in their roles.

Time-consuming technology

Technology is continually improving, and new improved equipment and devices are continually being produced. As such, the coach and manager need to decide what to invest in and then learn how to use the new products. The information produced by the devices then has to be analysed effectively to provide meaningful and useful data. This all takes time and means the coach and manager have to take time away from actual coaching.

Keeping up with developments in technology

There are usually a range of brands that produce a similar product, and each have their advantages and disadvantages. There are also individual new products to consider which can measure or monitor new areas of a participant's performance. The coach and manager need to be able to make informed decisions about which technologies to adopt to help to support their players. This all takes time and energy to keep up to date with the fast pace of technological change and development.

ACTIVITY

Select a piece of technology that you know has been developed over a period of time, such as a mobile phone. Carry out research to find out what that piece of technology could originally do and the cost of the technology, and compare this to how it has developed over the years in relation to what it is now able to do and its cost. Write a report that assesses the advantages and disadvantages of this development in technology. Add a conclusion which explains if you think the advances in technology have been beneficial for the people who use the technology.

Technology breakdowns and repair costs

Once the technology is in place it has to be maintained: this means some coaches and managers need to invest in a technician to keep the technology working appropriately and effectively. Occasionally the technology may break down which means it cannot be used at that time and there may be repair costs.

Cost of advanced technology

The initial cost of the technology can be very expensive. However, there are also costs involved in using the technology. This may mean that not all participants in an organisation will have access to this technology. In competitive leagues, some teams in the same league may have different budgets which means some coaches and managers will have access to advanced technology which can improve performance for their team. However, other teams may not have this kind of money and cannot afford the cost of advanced technology, so their players are disadvantaged.

The officials

While technology is used to support officials in making decisions as well as to help them carry out their role effectively, it can provide some areas for concern. This is because it can affect the flow of the game or the cost of the technology can limit its use.

Breaks in play

When technology is used in a game situation it can disrupt the flow of a game and slow it down. This is because it can mean time needs to be spent reviewing the data provided by the technology to make a decision. This is in contrast to the official seeing the situation and making an almost instantaneous decision based on what they saw first-hand. This break in the game means the official has to stop suddenly when they have been consistently moving around to keep up with the game, for example in rugby and football. This can lead to a decrease in cardiovascular demands on their body as the sudden stop in play means their heart rate would drop quite quickly. In turn, this can lead to them feeling dizzy or at risk of fainting. This is because the blood return to the heart is negatively affected by a sudden stop in activity.

Some technology is only available for certain levels

While new technology is being developed, in some sports it is only available at the elite level. For example, goal-line technology is only available to officials working with elite teams; however, grass roots officials would benefit from this technology too, but it is too expensive.

CHECK MY LEARNING

Select a sport or activity of your choice. Explain the advantages and disadvantages of technological advances in your selected sport for the officials in the sport and also the coach and manager. Ensure you give examples of each piece of technology and how it is used in that sport or activity in your response.

Learning aim C: assessment practice

How you will be assessed

This part of the component will involve research into the sport sector. You may be able to carry out research which involves visits to sports providers so that you can see and experience the differences in provision for public, private and voluntary providers. Information for each sector is also available online and in books.

You will also need to explore the advantages and disadvantages of up to four different uses of technology in sport and be able to explain the use of each one.

CHECKPOINT

Strengthen

- Describe the different uses of technology of sport and the advantages of each.
- Identify which people would benefit from the technology that has been described: participants, officials or coach and manager.
- Explain the disadvantages of technology in sport.

Challenge

- Analyse how developments in technology can improve participants' performance.
- Analyse how developments in technology can have a negative impact on the performance or selection of a sports performer.
- Assess how technology has been beneficial to officials and coaches and managers.

ASSESSMENT ACTIVITY   LEARNING AIM   C

For a sport or activity that you enjoy taking part in or watching, carry out research to find out about the following related to this selected sport and how it has developed over the years:

- the equipment used
- the protection used
- the clothing worn
- the footwear worn
- the facilities used for participants
- cameras, computers and software used.

Write an overview from your research that:

- identifies the equipment, protection, clothing, footwear, facilities and computing technology for the selected sport or activity
- explains how the technology has developed over the years
- explains the advantages of this development for the participants, coach and officials
- explains the disadvantages of these developments for the participants, coach and officials.

TIPS

When you are carrying out your research, consider if your selected sport or activity has any key events where participants compete at particular times of the year or over a period of years, such as the Olympics or the Tour de France. You can then search the winning times, distances or heights from the past and compare them to today's data. You can also examine the clothing, footwear and equipment that was used in the past from images of the winning competitors and compare these to the winners of today to help you with your research.

TAKE IT FURTHER

Explore ways in which new equipment, protection, clothing, footwear, facilities, cameras, computers and/or software could be developed to help improve performance even further for your selected sport or activity. Explain how these improvements are advantageous for the participant, the coach and/or the officials for your selected sport.

COMPONENT

02

The Principles of Training, Nutrition and Psychology for Sport and Activity

Introduction

Component 2 will explore the factors that contribute to improved fitness for sport and activity, including the importance of a healthy diet, and psychological factors. Fitness testing will be explored, looking at different ways to test a variety of components of fitness. You will also explore a range of training methods that can be used to develop specific components of fitness and look at how these support improvements in sport and activity performance.

Nutrition will also be covered in relation to health and well-being, as well as how nutrients can help to improve sport and activity performance. You will learn about the importance and functions of macronutrients and key micronutrients, and the food sources of each. Hydration will also be explored, relating the benefits of hydration to sport and activity performance. This will all help you to assess nutritional intake and provide recommendations to help improve nutritional intake for participants who take part in specific sports and activities.

Lastly, this component explores psychology and motivation. You will look at how self-confidence and anxiety have an effect on sport and activity performance, and at ways to optimise psychological factors to support improvements in performance.

Interpreting fitness data in relation to sport and activity: components of fitness (1)

A person can have high levels of fitness in some areas, such as flexibility, but less in others.

Fitness is a complicated subject. Many people consider it to be simply how far we can run, swim, cycle or row. However, the distance a person can complete is only a part of the overall elements that make someone fit. Someone can have high levels of fitness in one area and low levels of fitness in another area.

Fitness can be broken down into seven different components:

Figure 2.1: Fitness is made up of seven components

Aerobic endurance

Aerobic endurance is also known as cardiovascular fitness. It is the ability of the cardiorespiratory system to work efficiently, supplying nutrients and oxygen to working muscles during **sustained physical activity**.

Our muscular system is complex: it is made up of a large number of muscles.

Muscular endurance

Muscular endurance is related to how efficiently your muscular system works. The greater a person's muscular endurance, the increased ability they have to perform an exercise that involves repetitive contractions of a muscle over an extended period of time. Because there are many muscles in our body, it is possible to have good muscular endurance over one movement but poor over another. Movements could include squatting, performing a pull-up, doing a press-up or doing sit-ups.

◘ Table 2.1: Examples of sports that require good levels of muscular endurance

Individual sport	Team sport
Rock climbing to hold on to the rock face	Rugby to be able to keep pushing in a ruck or scrum
Hurdles to maintain the ability to jump	Hockey to ensure that participants can keep moving at speed
Swimming to keep up speed	Rowing to keep stroke rate high
Sailing to allow the person to lean out and keep the boat flat	Netball to allow athlete to keep jumping to catch the ball
Cycling to keep pushing the pedals and keep the bike moving	Football to allow competitors to keep kicking the ball hard

ACTIVITY

Muscular endurance is needed in everyday life. For example, when climbing a flight of stairs your leg muscles are repeatedly contracting to take you all the way up to the top of the stairs. Can you give any other examples of when muscular endurance might be needed in day-to-day life?

Strength

Strength is related to how much muscle mass a person has – the larger the muscle mass the more strength the person has. This is because muscle tissue produces force. The more muscle tissues that a person has, the more force their muscles can produce.

ACTIVITY

- Identify individual sports and team sports that require high levels of strength.
- For each sport, describe why the person playing that sport needs high levels of strength to perform well in their sport.

While it is not necessary to have high levels of strength for health reasons, a certain level of strength is required in order to support daily activities. Strong postural muscles are required to keep an upright stance and prevent back pains; strong leg muscles are required to allow us to hold our body weight and move around. Muscle tissue also has a high metabolic rate compared to other body tissues so it does help to 'burn calories' to prevent a person from becoming overweight. It is also important to note that as a person gets older, from about the age of 30, their muscle mass naturally starts to reduce unless the person takes part in resistance training to try and maintain or increase their muscle mass.

KEY TERM

Muscular endurance is where a muscle can continue contracting over a period of time against a light to moderate fixed resistance or load.

DID YOU KNOW?

There are between 640 and 850 muscles found within the human body, depending on what we count as being a muscle. The range in number is largely down to the difficulty in separating muscles that are grouped together and those that are distinct individual muscles.

KEY TERM

Strength is the maximum force (in kg or N) that can be generated by a muscle or muscle group.

CHECK MY LEARNING

1 List the seven components of fitness.
2 Explain why aerobic endurance is needed for any sports that have sustained physical activity.
3 For two sports of your choice, describe why specific areas of your body require high levels of muscular endurance.
4 For two sports of your choice, describe why specific areas of your body require high levels of strength.

Interpreting fitness data in relation to sport and activity: components of fitness (2)

Flexibility

Flexibility is an area of fitness that is sometimes overlooked in favour of increasing other components of fitness. However, being flexible is directly linked to success in almost every sport.

We have a greater range of motion available at some joints such as the shoulder compared to the elbow. You can move your whole arm in a circular motion because of the type of joint at the shoulder, whereas it is only possible to bend and straighten the elbow joint. Muscle and ligaments surround a joint and will affect how much movement a person can produce at a joint. The less flexible a person is the less movement they have at various joints in their bodies because their muscle tissues and ligaments are stiffer and shorter compared to a more flexible person.

Flexibility, like many other components of fitness, can be good across one area of a person's body but weak in another. Ensuring adequate flexibility is an important part of injury prevention. Forcing muscles to make movements that they are unused to can lead to damage and injury. Conditioning muscles with flexibility training can protect the body from injuries through over extension. During a warm-up, gently stretching muscles to prepare them for exercise should be an integral element.

> ACTIVITY
>
> Describe five sports and/or activities that require high levels of flexibility and the joints of the body that need to be flexible in order to be effective in each sport or activity.

Body composition

Body composition is what your body is made of. The main components of your body include bone, muscle and fat.

> ACTIVITY
>
> Chris Froome (Tour de France cyclist), Jessica Ennis-Hill (track and field athlete) and Owen Farrell (rugby player) are very clearly different athletes. What is it about their body compositions that make them effective at their chosen sports?

To a certain extent we are born with a body type and this will define our capabilities, strengths and weaknesses as an athlete. When you measure body composition, the main area that is considered is the amount of body fat a person has. You need to have some body fat to be healthy; however, too much body fat can result in health problems. An excess of body fat also increases our body's weight which in turn means that we have to carry more load. This extra load can make some sports, physical activities or daily tasks more difficult to complete.

Body composition can have a significant effect on a sports person's performance.

◼ **Table 2.2: Examples of sports that favour different body compositions**

Marathon runner

Long distance runners tend to have slight frames with lean muscles and carry very little body fat. This means that their legs need to work less hard to carry their frames than if they had muscly bodies or excess body fat.

Gymnast

Gymnasts have powerful frames with a lot of muscle tissue and very little body fat. By having low levels of body fat, gymnasts remain as light as possible but still have the muscle strength to jump high enough and with sufficient power to perform somersaults in the air.

Shot putter

An athlete that throws the shot put needs high levels of muscle tissue to throw the shot with force so it will travel a long distance. As they do not have to move their body any significant distance, excess body fat does not reduce the shot putter's performance.

CHECK MY LEARNING

1 Thinking about your own body, which areas are the most flexible and which areas are the least flexible? Explain why you think this is.

2 Explain how body composition affects performance in different sports and activities.

Interpreting fitness data in relation to sport and activity: components of fitness (3)

◘ **Elite 100-metre sprinters.**

Examine the photo of 100-metre women sprinters and identify key features of the sprinters' physique. Explain how these features help them to run at high speed over a short distance.

Speed

Speed is where a person travels very fast over a short distance. Speed is worked out by measuring distance covered divided by the time taken to cover the distance. Travelling at high speed can take place in various formats such as cycling, swimming, rowing or running over a short distance. Speed is also required in a range of team and individual sports and activities, such as having to sprint to get to the ball in football or to intercept a pass in netball.

◘ **Athletes who require a wheelchair can take part in wheelchair racing, which competes over short distances and requires high levels of speed.**

There are many sports that benefit from an athlete having speed. In a small group create a list of sports that require high levels of speed, from both team and individual sports and activities. Next to each, explain why high levels of speed are required.

Power

Power is a combination of strength and speed. In sport and activity terms, power is the ability to apply the maximum force possible in as fast a time as possible. The force applied can be into our own body, into someone else or into an object.

◘ **Table 2.3: Examples of individual sports that require high levels of power**

Golf needs power when a competitor has to hit the ball a long distance.	Shot put requires power to throw the shot.	Tennis requires power when hitting the ball, especially in the serve.
Sprinting involves high levels of power to accelerate from the blocks.	Power lifting is the ability to lift a weight quickly from the floor, often to above the head.	High jump needs power to push off the floor to generate height to get over the bar.

◘ **Table 2.4: Examples of team sports that require high levels of power**

Football players need power to kick the ball hard.	When rugby players are in the scrum and pushing against the other team they need power.	When playing netball, players need to have power to jump high enough to catch a pass.
Basketball requires lots of power to jump to the height of the basket and score.	Rowing requires power to accelerate up to speed and keep the boat moving fast.	Hockey involves lots of changes of direction. After every extreme change, a player needs power to accelerate again.

For three selected sports and/or activities that require high levels of power, explain how power is used in each sport.

1 Explain the difference between strength and power.
2 Explain why the more muscle mass a person has, the stronger they will be.

Interpreting fitness data in relation to sport and activity: normative data tables

Fitness testing

There are a variety of reasons for fitness testing; however, the main reason is usually to test a person's components of fitness to determine their strengths and also which components need to be developed. This information is then used to design training programmes to help to maintain the components of fitness that are at the appropriate level, as well as improve components of fitness that are not at the appropriate level, to help that person perform at their best in their selected sport or activity.

Fitness tests are designed to test specific components of fitness. For each test there will be particular equipment. There will also be a protocol, which is a set way of carrying out the test. The protocol should be followed exactly as it is written. This can include:

- setting out the fitness testing area or course
- ensuring it is measured out properly
- ensuring the person taking the fitness test is prepared appropriately
- following the protocol to ensure the fitness test process is carried out correctly.

The person administering the test will need to provide the participant with clear instructions, observe and monitor the participant when they are taking part in the test to ensure they are completing the test correctly, and then record the test results accurately.

◘ The person administering the fitness test must carefully observe and monitor the person taking part, whether at an amateur level or when working with professional athletes.

Interpreting fitness test results

Once the test results have been recorded, these will need to be interpreted to determine how well the participant has done compared with other people of the same age and gender. To do this, you will need to use **normative data**; this provides a benchmark to be able to assess the results and determine the fitness levels of the individual.

Normative data tables

For every fitness test there are published normative data tables. They are usually compiled from average results of people taking part in the fitness test. These normative data tables help to provide a guide to interpreting what the results mean and working out how well a person has performed by comparing their performance with the data in the tables. Often there will be categories of 'average', 'below average' and 'above average', with variations above these values such as 'excellent' and below these values such as 'poor'.

The tables are usually devised so they are specific to males or females. This takes into account the physiological differences between most males and females. Some normative data tables will also take age into account as this can also have an effect on performance for some components of fitness.

ACTIVITY

When people take part in any form of testing or when general population norms are taken, the results will usually show a similar shape to the one below.

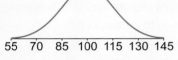

55 70 85 100 115 130 145

◻ **Figure 2.2: Normative data curve**

The results for most people fall within a similar range in the middle of the curve but some people have results that are either side of the curve. This shows that they have lower or higher results than the majority of the population.
- Collect data from people in your class which has a range of possible results, such as height or shoe size.
- Plot the data on a graph, with the variable measured on the x axis and the number of people with that reading on the y axis.
- Explain if your results show a similar path to the curve shown or if there are any differences.

Normative data tables are available for different groups of the population, such as the following examples.
- Girls and boys (14–16 years) – data tables are available for some fitness tests for girls and boys aged 14–16. As many girls and boys at these ages have not fully developed, it is important to use data tables that are age-appropriate as, for example, a 14-year-old boy would not be expected to have the same level of strength as a 21-year-old man.
- Men and women – most normative data tables provide separate data for men and women and are for the adult ages of 18–65. This data provides an overview of a person's performance related to the average population for other adult men and women.
- Norms for elite performers – elite performers are expected to have higher fitness levels as they take part in regular sport and physical activity and training that is specific to their selected sport. Elite performer normative data tables are therefore available to compare fitness test results across elite performers.
- Older people (65 years and older) – as a person gets older their fitness levels will decline. It is therefore necessary to have normative data tables that allow older people to compare their results to people of a similar age. For example, a 70-year-old female would not be expected to have the same level of aerobic endurance as a 20-year-old female.

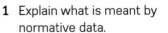

CHECK MY LEARNING

1 Explain what is meant by normative data.

2 Explain why it is necessary to have normative data tables for different groups of people, including girls and boys aged 14–16, men and women, elite sports performers and older people aged 65 or older.

Interpreting fitness data in relation to sport and activity: fitness tests (1)

KEY TERM

Reliability is the repeatability of results. If the test is repeated in exactly the same way, the same results should be achieved.

Cooper 12-minute run test to test aerobic endurance

This is a test that measures aerobic endurance. It involves running for as long a distance as possible within a 12-minute period of time, and then the distance covered is recorded. The Cooper 12-minute run is especially good for testing the aerobic fitness of people who take part in sports or activities that require lots of running, as the test replicates the same types of movements that are carried out in the sport. However, for a swimmer or cyclist this is not such a good test for measuring aerobic endurance as it uses running which swimmers and cyclists do not do in their sport.

The running surface and climate can affect the **reliability** of this test. A slippery surface or a hot day can make the test more difficult to complete and could result in lower scores.

This test can be carried out with more than one participant as all participants can run together – this can help with motivation if the athletes have a person they want to try to beat. The equipment is not expensive but the test does require access to a running track. The test is simple to set up and the protocol is easy to administer.

Equipment

- Athletics track
- Cones
- Whistle
- Stopwatch
- Tape measure

Protocol

Before taking part in the test, the participant should carry out an appropriate warm-up.

1 The participant stands at the starting line on the athletics track.
2 A whistle is blown by the person administering the test and the participant starts to run or jog around the track.
3 At 12 minutes, the whistle is blown and the participant stops running.
4 A cone is placed at the point where the participant stopped running.
5 The distance covered by the participant is measured and recorded to the nearest 10 metres.

 Table 2.5: Normative data for male athletes

Age	Excellent	Above average	Average	Below average	Poor
13–14	>2700 m	2400–2700 m	2200–2399 m	2100–2199 m	<2100 m
15–16	>2800 m	2500–2800 m	2300–2499 m	2200–2299 m	<2200 m
17–19	>3000 m	2700–3000 m	2500–2699 m	2300–2499 m	<2300 m
20–29	>2800 m	2400–2800 m	2200–2399 m	1600–2199 m	<1600 m
30–39	>2700 m	2300–2700 m	1900–2299 m	1500–1999 m	<1500 m
40–49	>2500 m	2100–2500 m	1700–2099 m	1400–1699 m	<1400 m
>50	>2400 m	2000–2400 m	1600–1999 m	1300–1599 m	<1300 m

■ Table 2.6: Normative data for female athletes

Age	Excellent	Above average	Average	Below average	Poor
13–14	>2000 m	1900–2000 m	1600–1899 m	1500–1599 m	<1500 m
15–16	>2100 m	2000–2100 m	1700–1999 m	1600–1699 m	<1600 m
17–20	>2300 m	2100–2300 m	1800–2099 m	1700–1799 m	<1700 m
20–29	>2700 m	2200–2700 m	1800–2199 m	1500–1799 m	<1500 m
30–39	>2500 m	2000–2500 m	1700–1999 m	1400–1699 m	<1400 m
40–49	>2300 m	1900–2300 m	1500–1899 m	1200–1499 m	<1200 m
>50	>2200 m	1700–2200 m	1400–1699 m	1100–1399 m	<1100 m

ACTIVITY

Take part in the Cooper 12-minute run test. Record your result for the test and compare it to the appropriate normative data table.

Sit and reach test to test flexibility

This test measures the flexibility of the muscles in the lower back and hamstrings, and therefore provides an overview of a person's flexibility. However, a person may be much more flexible in other areas of their body, or the sport or activity they take part in requires high levels of flexibility in other areas of the body. The reliability of these test results depends on how much time has been spent on the warm-up. The warmer a person is the more flexible they are. Minimal equipment is required: only a sit and reach box which is not expensive. The test is quick and easy to perform and can be carried out in most places.

■ Figure 2.3: The sit and reach test measures the flexibility of the lower back and hamstrings

Equipment
- Sit and reach box

Protocol
Before taking part in the test, the participant should carry out an appropriate warm-up.
1 The person taking the test should remove their shoes and make sure they are wearing clothing which does not restrict their movement.
2 The person should sit with their legs straight and their feet against the box.
3 Keeping their legs straight, the person slowly reaches as far forward as they possibly can, pushing the marker on the sit and reach box forward.
4 Record the furthest point the person is able to push the marker.
5 Repeat the test three times. The best result is the one that is used to compare to normative data tables.

ACTIVITY

Take part in the sit and reach test. Record your best result and compare it to the normative data table.

CHECK MY LEARNING

Explain what you have found out about your aerobic endurance and flexibility levels from taking part in the Cooper 12-minute run test and sit and reach test. Explain why you think you have achieved these results. For example, do the sports or physical activities that you take part in have an effect on your aerobic endurance and/or flexibility?

■ Table 2.7: Normative data for sit and reach test (males and females)

Rating	Males (cm)	Females (cm)
Excellent	+17 – +27	+21 – +30
Good	+6 – +16	+11 – +20
Average	0 – +5	+1 – +10
Fair	–8 – –1	–7 – 0
Poor	–20 – –9	–15 – –8
Very poor	<–20	<–15

Interpreting fitness data in relation to sport and activity: fitness tests (2)

One-minute sit-up test to test muscular endurance

This test measures the muscular endurance of the abdominal muscles. It requires high levels of motivation in order to push oneself to complete as many sit-ups as possible in the one-minute period. Minimal equipment is required – just a stopwatch and a mat. The test is quick and easy to perform and can be carried out in most places. Note that the test does not provide an overview of a person's overall muscular endurance as it mainly measures the muscular endurance of the abdominal muscles.

Equipment

- Mat
- Stopwatch

Protocol

Before taking part in the test, the participant should carry out an appropriate warm-up.

1 The person taking the test lies with their back on the floor with their hands on their chest and their knees bent.

2 On the command of 'go' the stopwatch is started and the person sits up until their elbows touch their knees.

3 They return to the start position with the back of their head touching the floor. This constitutes one repetition.

4 The person does as many sit-ups as they can in one minute.

5 The number of sit-ups completed in one minute is recorded.

◘ Figure 2.4: The one-minute sit-up test is quick and easy to perform

◘ Table 2.8: Normative data for one-minute sit-up test

Rating	Males (no. of reps)	Females (no. of reps)
Excellent	49–59	42–54
Good	43–48	36–41
Above average	39–42	32–35
Average	35–38	28–31
Below average	31–34	24–27
Poor	25–30	18–23
Very poor	11–24	3–17

Hand grip dynamometer test to test strength

This test uses a grip dynamometer to measure hand grip strength.

The dynamometer needs to be adjusted so that it is set at the right size for the person who is taking the test, to ensure it provides reliable data. The technique to perform the test needs to remain the same and the same rest periods between each test need to be given in order to compare results. Minimal equipment is required, just the hand grip dynamometer. The test is quick and easy to perform and can be carried out in most places. The test only measures the strength of the forearms and hands so it does not provide a measure of general strength, as the strength of the forearms does not always represent the strength of different muscle groups in the body. If a person is right or left handed this can affect the results: the stronger hand/arm is usually the dominant one.

Equipment

- Hand grip dynamometer

Protocol

1 The handle should be adjusted so that it fits the size of the hand of the person being tested.

2 The dynamometer should be held in the dominant hand and the arm kept hanging by their side with the dynamometer by their thigh.

3 The person should squeeze the dynamometer as hard as they can for around 5 seconds.

4 The results should be recorded.

5 Rest for at least 1 minute.

6 Repeat the test two more times with at least a 1-minute rest period between each test.

7 Record each result.

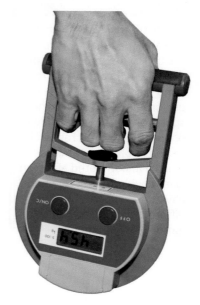

■ The only equipment needed for this test is the hand grip dynamometer.

■ Table 2.9: Normative data for grip strength

Rating	Males aged 15–19 years (kgw)	Females aged 15–19 years (kgw)
Excellent	>52	>32
Good	47–51	28–31
Average	44–46	25–27
Below average	39–43	20–24
Poor	<39	<20

CHECK MY LEARNING

The following two sports people want to measure their muscular endurance and strength: a tennis player and a long-distance cyclist. Explain if the one-minute sit-up test and hand grip dynamometer are suitable tests to measure the muscular endurance and strength of these two sports performers.

Interpreting fitness data in relation to sport and activity: fitness tests (3)

Sergeant jump test to test power

The sergeant jump test is also known as the vertical jump test. This test is a good way to assess a person's power in their legs. The test is quick and easy to perform, and it does not require any expensive equipment. Jumping technique, however, can have an effect on the results: the better the technique the better the results. It is therefore important that a person has a number of practice jumps to develop their technique. The test just measures the power in the legs and does not test for upper body strength.

Equipment

- Wall
- Chalk
- Ruler or tape measure

Protocol

Before taking part in the test, the person must make sure they are fully warmed up.

1 The person taking the test stands side on to the wall, keeping their feet flat on the floor.
2 With the hand closest to the wall, they need to reach as high as they can and the test administrator should mark where the person's stretched fingers come to.
3 The person taking the test should then cover the fingers of the hand that is going to be next to the wall with chalk.
4 Standing side on next to the wall, they then need to bend down and jump up as high as possible. At the highest point in the air, the person needs to touch the wall so they leave a chalk mark to show how high they have jumped.
5 The difference between the first mark taken and the chalk mark is the score for this fitness test.

■ Figure 2.5: The sergeant jump test is used to test power in the legs

■ Table 2.10: Normative data for sergeant jump test (men and women aged 16–19)

Gender	Excellent	Above average	Average	Below average	Poor
Male	>65 cm	50–65 cm	40–49 cm	30–39 cm	<30 cm
Female	>58 cm	47–58 cm	36–46 cm	26–35 cm	<26 cm

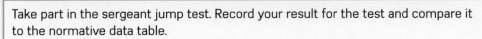

ACTIVITY

Take part in the sergeant jump test. Record your result for the test and compare it to the normative data table.

30-metre sprint test to test speed

This is a useful test to measure speed. It does not require any expensive equipment and is quick and easy to perform. The surface that the fitness test takes place on can affect the results, for example if it is slippery or bumpy. Therefore a running track or indoor sports hall are often used to ensure that the results are not negatively affected by the running surface.

Equipment

- Suitable flat non-slip running surface
- Tape measure
- Stopwatch

Protocol

Before taking the test, the person should thoroughly warm up.

1 The person starts behind the line in a stationary position.

2 The person administering the test stands at the finishing line and shouts 'Go' as they start the stopwatch.

3 The person sprints as fast as they can over the 30-metre distance.

4 The person administering the test stops the stopwatch when they see the person taking the test passing the line.

5 The results are recorded. The person has a 3-minute rest period and then repeats the test.

6 The best result from the two tests is recorded.

◻ Table 2.11: Normative data for 30-metre sprint test

30-metre sprint rating	Male	Female
Excellent	<4.0 s	<4.5 s
Above average	4.2–4.0 s	4.6–4.5 s
Average	4.4–4.3 s	4.8–4.7 s
Below average	4.6–4.5 s	5.0–4.9 s
Poor	<4.6 s	<5.0 s

Source: Davis B et al: Physical Education and the Study of Sport; 2000

ACTIVITY

Take part in the 30-metre sprint test. Record your result for the test and compare it to the normative data table.

CHECK MY LEARNING

1 Explain why it is important for a person to have a few practice jumps before taking part in the sergeant jump test and recording their result.

2 Describe why it is important for the 30-metre sprint test to take place on a non-slippery floor.

3 Assess if you think the sergeant jump test and 30-metre sprint test would be suitable fitness tests to measure power and speed in the following sports: basketball and swimming.

Interpreting fitness data: fitness test score and its impact on sport and activity

We have explored a variety of tests for different components of fitness. Some of the fitness test results have an impact on the person taking part in a particular sport or activity. Where results are not so good and the component of fitness is one which is needed to allow the person to do well in a selected sport or activity, it is important to check if the fitness test used provides meaningful results related to that person's sport or activity.

Participation in certain sports or physical activities may mean some fitness tests are a more valid indicator of the component of fitness than others. For example:

- the 12-minute run is appropriate to measure aerobic endurance in a person who takes part in sports involving continuous periods of running, such as a cross-country runner
- the hand grip dynamometer is useful to test strength in someone who takes part in sports or physical activities that require high levels of forearm strength for a strong grip, such as on a racket, e.g. in tennis, badminton, squash
- the one-minute sit-up test is appropriate for a person who needs high levels of core strength, such as a boxer
- the sit and reach test measures the flexibility of the hamstrings and lower back but does not provide any information regarding flexibility in other areas of the body; therefore this test is less important for, say, a swimmer who competes using the butterfly stroke and needs good flexibility in the shoulders.

However, while these fitness tests do not always test the right areas of the body, they do provide an overview of a person's levels of overall fitness. Often, if a person scores high results in a fitness test for a specific body area, such as the sit and reach test, it will indicate that the person being tested has good all-round flexibility. If it has been confirmed that they have excellent flexibility in their lower back and hamstrings, this probably shows that they do take part in flexibility training and are therefore likely to have high levels of flexibility in other areas of the body too.

◼ A person performing the one-minute sit-up test.

ACTIVITY

For the following scenarios:
- identify which component of fitness is being tested by each fitness test
- use the appropriate normative data tables to assess the fitness test results
- explain why each component being tested is required for the selected sport or activity.

Scenario 1

Kit is a 16-year-old rugby player. The results of his fitness tests are shown in Table 2.12.

Table 2.12: Kit's fitness test results

Fitness test	Fitness test result
Hand grip dynamometer test	47
Sergeant jump test	62 cm
30-metre sprint test	<3.5 s

Scenario 2

Julie is a 23-year-old swimmer. She competes in butterfly races. The results of her fitness tests are shown in Table 2.13.

Table 2.13: Julie's fitness test results

Fitness test	Fitness test result
One-minute sit-up test	36 reps
Cooper 12-minute run test	1800 m
Sit and reach test	23 cm

Having low levels of the components of fitness that are being tested can have a negative impact on sport or activity performance. It may well mean that other people taking part in that sport or activity will perform better because they have higher levels of fitness in specific components. It is therefore important to carry out fitness testing in order to be able to work out which components of fitness need to be improved.

CHECK MY LEARNING

For the following sports and activities, identify which components of fitness are required to perform effectively and provide examples of how they can be tested and assessed:
- hockey
- tennis
- high jump
- steeplechase.

Methods of training for sport and activity: aerobic endurance

GETTING STARTED

Make a list of sports and activities that involve at least 30 minutes or more of physical activity.

Next to each sport and activity, write down how long each one typically lasts.

The term endurance means the ability to sustain an activity for a period of time. Endurance usually relates to sports and activities that last for around 30 minutes or longer. Aerobic endurance is related to the cardiorespiratory system and muscular endurance is related to the muscular system. For many sports and activities that require endurance, both aerobic endurance is required and muscular endurance in the muscles that are being used to perform the sport or activity for a long time.

Aerobic endurance training

There are many ways to train for aerobic endurance. Our heart is a muscle and the respiratory system also includes muscles. Just like other muscles in our body, they can be strengthened through exercise. However, to strengthen the muscles in the cardiorespiratory system, the activity performed has to be at an intensity to increase our breathing and heart rate and carried out for a minimal period of time.

Continuous training

This is when we work the body at a constant intensity for a sustained period of time, usually over 30 minutes. This could be jogging, cycling or swimming for example, for at least 30 minutes.

During continuous training a person's heart rate should be kept at a rate where it is working hard but not over working – this is at 60–80 per cent of maximum heart rate. To help to calculate this intensity, a monitor to measure heart rate (beats per minute or bpm) can be used together with working out your **maximum heart rate**.

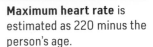

KEY TERM

Maximum heart rate is estimated as 220 minus the person's age.

ACTIVITY

Find out what 60–80% of your maximum heart rate is.
- Work out your maximum heart rate:

Maximum heart rate = 220 – your age.

For example, a person aged 25 would have a maximum heart rate of
220 – 25 = 195 bpm
- To work out 60% of your maximum heart rate use the following equation:

Your maximum heart rate $\times \dfrac{60}{100}$
- To work out 80% of your maximum heart rate use the following equation:

Your maximum heart rate $\times \dfrac{80}{100}$

Interval training

This involves exercising at a high intensity followed by a recovery period. The exercise time can vary from 30 seconds to 5 minutes followed by a recovery period which can involve complete rest or exercising at a very low intensity such as walking or light jogging. The exercise intervals will be at an intensity of around 60–80 per cent of a person's maximum heart rate. To increase aerobic endurance, the number of rest periods are decreased, and work intensity is decreased.

Fartlek training

Fartlek means 'speed play' in Swedish. It combines continuous training with interval training. Fartlek training mixes periods of low intensity work with higher intensity to push the body. The intensity can be varied by travelling at different speeds or over different terrain, such as up and down hills. The training is continuous with no rest period. The use of equipment such as a harness, running with weights or running with a weighted backpack can also be used in Fartlek training to increase the intensity. It is suitable for both absolute beginners as well as professional athletes to improve aerobic endurance. This form of training can be done on a rowing machine, bike, by swimming, running, or in any other way that raises the heart rate. Intensity can also be changed.

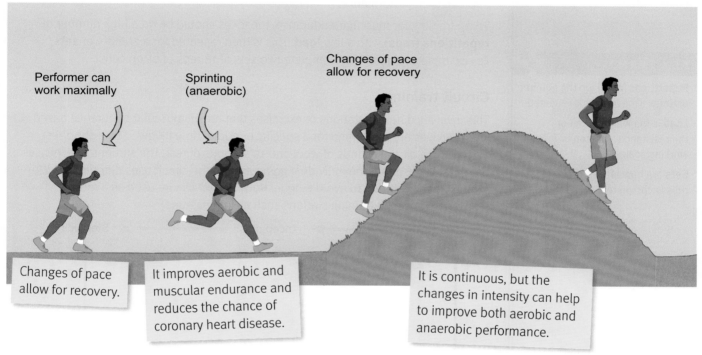

Performer can work maximally

Sprinting (anaerobic)

Changes of pace allow for recovery

Changes of pace allow for recovery.

It improves aerobic and muscular endurance and reduces the chance of coronary heart disease.

It is continuous, but the changes in intensity can help to improve both aerobic and anaerobic performance.

 Figure 2.6: Fartlek training mixes continuous training with interval training

CHECK MY LEARNING

1 For a sport of your choice, explain the type of exercise and how long you would carry it out for the following types of training:
   • continuous training
   • fartlek training
   • interval training.

2 Explain why it is important to monitor heart rate when a person is carrying out continuous training.

3 Explain the difference between interval training and fartlek training.

Methods of training for sport and activity: muscular endurance

With a partner, think about what is meant by muscular endurance. Make a list of sports that you think would require high levels of muscular endurance, giving reasons for each choice.

KEY TERMS

Repetitions (reps) are the number of times a movement is repeated.

Load is the weight lifted or the resistance a person is working against.

Sets are how often a group of reps is completed.

Muscular endurance training

Muscular endurance is the ability of a muscle or muscle groups to be able to contract repeatedly for long periods of time. A cyclist, for example, would need good muscular endurance in their leg muscles to keep pushing the pedals round to travel long distances. The muscles that are required for a participant's selected sport or activity will therefore need to be focused on in muscular endurance training to help to improve their performance.

When training for muscular endurance, the focus should be on a high number of **repetitions (reps)** with a low **load**. This is then repeated for a number of **sets**. For example, a person may complete two sets of 18 reps of bicep curls.

Circuit training

This involves different stations or exercises that are all muscular endurance based. The exercises are performed for a specific period of time followed by a short rest period, such as 45 seconds of work and 15 seconds of rest. The stations or exercises are organised so that the individual going around the circuit uses different muscle groups at each station to avoid fatigue. Body weight can be used as a form of resistance for circuit training stations such as in press-ups.

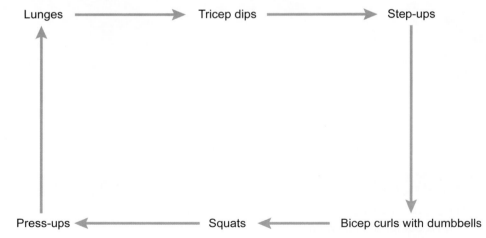

■ Figure 2.7: A muscular endurance training circuit like this uses different muscle groups at each station to avoid muscle fatigue

Core stability training

The core muscles stabilise the spine and help to reduce any postural imbalances, which helps to prevent injuries from occurring. There are many different types of core stability training available which concentrate on working the deep muscles of the stomach and the back, as shown in Figure 2.8.

Side plank

Floating triangle

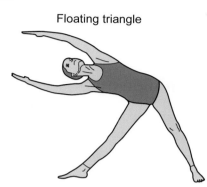

Dolphin

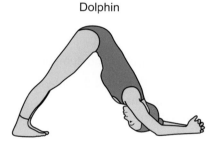

Locust

Boat

◘ Figure 2.8: Examples of exercises which work the core muscles

CHECK MY LEARNING

1 Design a muscular endurance circuit which uses six different stations from those shown in Figure 2.7.

2 Place them in a circuit order so that different muscle groups are used in each consecutive station, with one station to work on core stability.

Methods of training for sport and activity: strength and power

The amount of force a person can exert is related to the size of their muscles. The larger the muscles the more force can be produced. This is what strength is all about – the amount of force a person can produce. Power is related to strength; however, power is how fast the person can produce the force. As such, strength and power are trained in different ways.

Strength training

To increase strength, muscle tissue needs to be overloaded by using heavy weights, which has the effect of causing muscle **hypertrophy**.

A person should be of sufficient age and maturity to start a strength training programme. For any type of strength training, the principle remains the same in that a person needs to carry out low reps using high weights. To start with, a person would find their **1 rep max (1RM)** and then use weights that are usually around 75 per cent of their 1RM. They would carry out a number of sets, sometimes increasing or decreasing the load depending on the type of strength training they are using.

Free weights

A free weight is one that is not attached to machinery, such as barbells and dumbbells.

A barbell is a long bar with weights at either end, used with both hands; dumbbells are shorter with weights at either end and are used one in each hand. Dumbbells can be used to perform **dynamic exercises** to strengthen different muscle groups. For example, bicep curls are used to strengthen the biceps, a chest press is used to strengthen the chest muscles, etc.

Fixed resistance machines

Fixed resistance machines use stacks of weights attached to pulleys or air pressure to provide resistance. This type of strength training equipment provides set types of exercises that only permit movement for a specific exercise. For example, the fixed resistance machine in the photograph only permits the hamstring curl movement pattern as shown.

Power training

Power training movements use a lighter weight compared with strength training but one that allows the person to perform a high number of repetitions to simulate repeated use of power in competition.

Plyometrics

Plyometric training is any exercise that enables a muscle to reach maximum force in the fastest possible time. Just before the movement the muscles about to be used are stretched or lengthened and then shortened rapidly to make the movement. The shorter the time between the stretching phase and shortening the more power can be generated. This sort of training is usually carried out by jumping on and off benches and steps (Figure 2.9). As the person lands the muscle is lengthened and then it contracts and shortens to allow the person to jump up onto the next bench or step.

You will need to ensure you have no injuries and are fully fit and warmed up before taking part in this.

Complete some of the plyometric training techniques shown in Table 2.14. Complete the table with the muscles that are being worked in the activity and which sport or activities this type of power training would be useful for.

◘   Table 2.14: Plyometric training techniques

Plyometric activity	Description	Muscles used	Sport or activity that would benefit from this type of training
Box jumps	Stand with your feet side by side. In a fluid motion jump up and forwards onto a box at least knee height. Step back down and repeat.		
Wall balls	Hold a medicine ball at chest height. Bend to a squat position and then stand straight pushing with your arms to propel the ball to a point above your head on the wall. Catch and repeat.		
Jump push-ups	Hold yourself in a press-up position with arms extended. Lower your chest smoothly to the floor and then push back up as hard as you can, aiming for your hands to leave the ground at the top of the movement.		

◘ Figure 2.9: Plyometric training is often carried out by jumping on and off benches or steps

Anaerobic hill sprints

This type of training requires access to a hill. How steep the hill is will have an impact on the level of intensity required to sprint up it; a steeper hill will require much more effort compared to a hill with a more gradual incline. It is called **anaerobic** as the energy systems used to provide energy for this training do not require oxygen.

For this training, the person simply needs to run as fast as possible up the hill and then have a recovery period walking back down the hill. They will then repeat this process a number of times.

CrossFit®

This is a brand of training which was founded by Greg Glassman and Lauren Jenai. It contains a variety of exercises which include using body weight as a form of resistance, weightlifting and also aerobic exercises. A huge range of equipment can be used such as kettlebells, dumbbells, rowing machines and medicine balls to add variety and interest to the training. It also allows specific areas to be focused on if a person is wanting to train key areas of their body for strength and power.

Consider the sport of volleyball. Explain the different methods of strength and power training and the muscle groups that should be trained in order to help to improve volleyball performance.

Methods of training for sport and activity: flexibility

Flexibility training

Flexibility is an area of fitness that is sometimes overlooked in favour of increasing other components of fitness. However, being flexible is directly linked to success in almost every sport.

Ensuring adequate flexibility is also an important part of injury prevention. Forcing muscles, tendons and ligaments to make movements that they are unused to can lead to damage and injury.

Flexibility training involves different types of stretching. There are three main types: **static**, **dynamic** and proprioceptive neuromuscular facilitation.

Static stretching

This is where a person gets into a specific position to target a particular muscle or muscle group, and holds that position to develop the stretch. A person can use their own body to hold the muscle in a stretched position, such as holding one arm across the body to stretch the shoulder. They can also use another person or object to hold the body part in the correct position to stretch the targeted muscle(s), usually for a period of around 12 to 30 seconds.

◘ A bench can be used to hold the body in position to stretch the hamstrings.

Dynamic stretching

This type of stretching involves gradually increasing the range of movement of a muscle or group of muscles over a series of repetitions. This must be done in a controlled and smooth manner to ensure safety. An example of a dynamic stretch would be to carry out repeated walking hamstring curls.

Proprioceptive neuromuscular facilitation (PNF) stretching

This type of stretching is usually performed in the cool-down part of a training session to develop the length of the muscle. This method of stretching requires the help of a partner or an immovable object to provide resistance. The participant stretches their muscle as far as possible. A partner then helps by holding the body part being stretched. The participant then pushes their stretched body part against their partner for 6–10 seconds while the partner resists the movement. The muscle is then relaxed as the partner pushes the body part to increase the stretch. This process is repeated approximately three times.

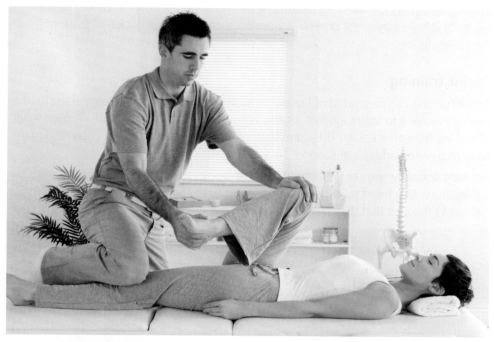

◻ **A partner can provide resistance during PNF stretching.**

ACTIVITY

Carry out research to find out what sort of classes are available to develop a person's flexibility.

In your research find out what is available, the type of stretching included in the class and how it develops flexibility. Also find out how long the class lasts and the cost.

Explain how useful you think flexibility-related exercise classes are for a person who takes part in regular sport and activity.

CHECK MY LEARNING ■ ■

Think about your own levels of flexibility and the sport or activity that you take part in. Select a flexibility training method that you think would be most appropriate to meet your needs and explain why you have chosen this flexibility training method.

Methods of training for sport and activity: speed

Speed training

Speed is the ability to cover a set distance as quickly as possible. Athletic track events are all about covering a set distance faster than the other competitors, such as in a 100-metre sprint. However, speed is also important in many different types of sport and activity, such as being able to sprint to the ball before an opponent in football or sprinting to intercept a ball thrown by an opposing team.

Interval training

This type of training has been covered before in relation to improving aerobic endurance. The training still involves periods of exercise and rest. However, when training for speed, the exercise periods all involve sprinting short distances at high intensity followed by a rest or recovery period such as jogging back to the start of the sprinting line.

Sprint training

Sprint training can be carried out using some form of resistance to increase the load a person is having to sprint against, or alternatively assisted sprinting, which uses ways of making the sprint easier. These are both recognised techniques for encouraging the body to develop additional speed.

Resisted sprinting uses equipment to hold the person back, for example a sled or a parachute. This helps to target the muscles used to complete the sprinting and overloads them so that they become stronger.

▣ Equipment which holds the person back provides resistance, therefore helping to make the muscles used stronger.

Assisted sprinting can include running downhill or on a treadmill. This helps the muscles to get used to the actual process of moving at speed.

Sport-specific speed training (speed, agility and quickness, SAQ®)

In many sports it is necessary to be fast but also to be able to change direction quickly, which is where **agility** comes in.

To train for agility, sport-specific training can be carried out which includes SAQ® equipment and/or training principles. Essentially, the training involves sprinting and then changing direction over a set course. In basketball this may mean dribbling the ball while sprinting around cones set up on the court or having other people act as opponents and dribbling at speed around them while still guarding the ball. This represents the type of speed that is specific to the sport and includes sport-specific skills such as sprinting while dribbling the ball.

> **KEY TERM**
>
> **Agility** is the ability to change direction at speed without losing balance.

> **ACTIVITY**
>
> For the following sports performers, identify a suitable training method to develop speed and then explain why this method is the most appropriate training method for the sport.
> - a rugby player
> - a 100m sprinter
> - a netball player.

> **CHECK MY LEARNING**
>
> 1 Explain how three different types of equipment can be used to help to improve a person's speed.
> 2 Assess why it is beneficial for a netball player to carry out SAQ training as well as speed training.

Advantages and disadvantages of each method of training (1)

When taking part in any type of training, there are some advantages to the training method in relation to how easy it is to perform considering the equipment and environment required. There are also disadvantages in relation to how appropriate it is to the selected sport or activity, how interesting it is and the equipment requirements.

With the person sitting next to you, discuss the advantages and disadvantages of the training methods you have used or are taking part in for your selected sports and activities.

Aerobic endurance training

◪ Table 2.15: The advantages and disadvantages of types of aerobic endurance training

Type of aerobic endurance training	Continuous training	Fartlek training	Interval training
Sport-related advantages	Good for sports and activities that last at least 30 minutes		
	Good for sports that have long periods of time working at the same intensity	Good for sports that have varied intensity, from changes in speed or changes in intensity such as going up a hill	Good for sports that have varied intensity with recovery periods
Examples of related sports	10 km running, open water swimming, rowing, kayaking	Cross-country running, mountain biking	Team sports such as hockey – having to sprint for the ball then jog or walk back to position
Equipment-related advantages	No equipment needed other than equipment required to participate in selected sport, such as a bike for cycling Mostly this type of training will take place outside so no training facility required other than appropriate space and distances for the person to cover during training It can take place indoors on equipment such as a treadmill, exercise cycle, cross trainer, rowing machine		
Other advantages	Can be carried out by an individual at times that fit in with their other commitments		
		The participant can control their own pace and lower the intensity when they need to Less technical than interval training so easier to use Changing the intensity helps to vary the training so can feel less boring compared to continuous training.	Helps to plan for progression in a training programme by increasing the intensity of the work periods, the number of work periods or decreasing the rest periods
Sport-related disadvantages	Very few sports are carried out at the same intensity for the duration. Even in 10 km running the person may need to run fast for a sprint finish	There is no rest period in this type of training	
Equipment-related disadvantages	As this training usually takes place outside, the weather can impact performance. For example, cold, wet days may put people off training; too hot may cause the person to get tired too quickly		
Other disadvantages	Takes at least 30 minutes so people may not have enough time to complete on a regular basis		
		Can become tedious Higher risk of injury from running long distances on hard surfaces	

For a sport or activity of your choice, select one fitness training method to improve aerobic endurance, one fitness training method to improve muscular endurance and one to improve speed.

Explain your choice, giving the advantages and disadvantages for both the coach and the participant of each method of training selected.

Muscular endurance training

◘ Table 2.16: The advantages and disadvantages of types of muscular endurance training

Type of muscular endurance training	Circuit training	Core stability training
Sport-related advantages	The stations can be tailored to the specific activities and muscle groups used in the sport and include sports drills for each specific sport, so skills used in the sport can be included in the training	Core stability is required for participation in all sports and activities to maintain a good posture and help to prevent back-related injuries
Examples of related sports	Team sports such as volleyball, hockey, football, etc. and individual sports such as squash, fun runs	All sports
Equipment-related advantages	A wide range of equipment or bodyweight can be used as a form of resistance so costs can be minimal	No equipment is needed as most core stability exercises can be carried out using bodyweight alone. A stability ball can be used but these are very low cost
Other advantages	The stations can be varied, and the time spent on each station can change so this type of training is great for avoiding boredom	Can be carried out by an individual at times that fit in with their other commitments
Sport-related disadvantages	None	None
Equipment-related disadvantages	Usually some form of cards or signs are used to state what type of training needs to be carried out. These have to be prepared in advance of the training. Stations need to be arranged so that different muscle groups are trained at each station. It can take time to organise the circuit so that the stations are ordered correctly and in many cases different types of equipment are used to add variety to the training	None
Other disadvantages	This type of training is usually performed in a group exercise situation, which is beneficial for people who enjoy working out with other people but does limit the flexibility of the timing of this type of training	None

Speed training

◘ Table 2.17: The advantages and disadvantages of types of speed training

Type of speed training	Interval training	Sprint training	Sport-specific training
Sport-related advantages	Good for sports that have varied intensity with recovery periods	Good for sports that require travelling at speed	Can be made sports-specific so that the participant trains their speed while also including elements of their sport in the training, such as running at speed while dribbling a ball
Examples of related sports	Team sports such as hockey – having to sprint for the ball then jog or walk back to position	Good for sports that require sprinting in a line without having to change direction such as 100m sprint, long jump	Good for sports which require sprinting and changing direction at pace such as dodging an opponent, e.g. rugby, basketball, hockey
Equipment-related advantages	No equipment needed other than equipment required to participate in selected sport, such as a bike for cycling. Mostly this type of training will take place outside so no training facility required other than appropriate space and distances for the person to cover during training	Equipment can be used to add resistance but is not very expensive, such as bungee ropes, a sled or parachute, and does not take time to set up	Equipment is required but this may simply be cones set out for the participants to move around at speed. Equipment related to the sport that the participant plays is also required but this would be accessible as part of a usual training programme for that sport
Other advantages	Helps to plan for progression in a training programme by increasing the intensity of the work periods, number of work periods or decreasing the rest periods	The type of training using different types of equipment can be varied, which helps to avoid boredom	
Sport-related disadvantages	Does not always replicate the movements played in the sport as it does not usually include using sport-specific equipment as part of the training	Only useful for sprinting in one direction	None
Equipment-related disadvantages	None	The equipment is not expensive but will need to be bought and stored for use	A range of equipment can be bought to help with this type of training which can take some time to set up prior to use
Other disadvantages	This type of training is usually performed in a group exercise situation, which is beneficial for people who enjoy working out with other people but does limit the flexibility of the timing of this type of training		

Advantages and disadvantages of each method of training (2)

Strength training

■ Table 2.18: The advantages and disadvantages of types of strength training

Type of strength training	Free weights	Resistance machines
Sport-related advantages	Increase the strength over a large range of movements. Allow the person to focus on certain movements or specific muscle groups. Some movements help to improve coordination	Increase strength of targeted muscle groups used for a specific sport
Examples of related sports	Specific muscles and muscle groups can be targeted to help to increase strength in these areas and improve performance in a range of sports, e.g. a swimmer may want to increase the strength in their chest muscles to improve their breast stroke, a cricketer may want to increase the strength in their shoulder to help to increase their bowling performance	
Equipment-related advantages	Can be stored and used at home. The same equipment can be used to train different muscle groups	
Other advantages		Safer for people new to weight training as there is less chance of injury from not being able to lift the weight. Can train alone
Sport-related disadvantages	The movement carried out in the weight-training exercises will rarely replicate the movements carried out in the person's sport, so while the muscle size will increase in the targeted muscles, the actual range of movement used in the sport may not	
Equipment-related disadvantages	Initial costs to buy the barbell, dumbbells and weights. A spotter is needed to ensure the safety of the person taking part in the training, so it cannot be carried out alone	Most people will use fixed resistance machines in a gym as equipment is costly and also takes up a lot of room in one's home. Usually one machine exercises only one muscle or muscle group, so many different pieces of equipment are required for strength training across a range of muscle groups
Other disadvantages	There is a greater chance of not being able to lift the weight when fatigued and no spotter is in place, which could result in injury	

Flexibility training

■ Table 2.19: The advantages and disadvantages of types of flexibility training

Type of flexibility training	Static stretching	Dynamic stretching	PNF stretching
Sport-related advantages	Help to increase flexibility in specific areas required for a specific sport		
Examples of related sports	Increased range of movement permitted at the shoulders for a swimmer to perform the butterfly stroke, at the hips for a hurdler to be able to get into the right position when getting over a hurdle		
Equipment-related advantages	No equipment needed, so no costs or time spent having to set up equipment		
Other advantages		Helps to maintain an elevated heart rate so is a good form of stretching during the warm-up to help to get the body ready for training	Helps to develop flexibility at a faster rate compared to other types of flexibility training
Sport-related disadvantages	None		
Equipment-related disadvantages	None		Cannot be performed on own: needs another person to carry out the stretching process
Other disadvantages	None		Can increase the risk of injury if the person helping to support the stretching process has no experience of what to do

Power training

■ Table 2.20: The advantages and disadvantages of types of power training

Type of power training	Plyometrics	Anaerobic hill sprints	CrossFit ®
Sport-related advantages	Can be specific to the muscle groups that require power	Beneficial for sports that are carried out at high intensity and involve running	Can be made sport-specific
Examples of related sports	High jump, long jump, basketball, gymnastics	Cross-country running	Sprinting, shot put, gymnastics
Equipment-related advantages	The equipment is cheap and relatively easy to set up	No setting up or cost requirements	Equipment is relatively cheap and does not take long to set up
Other advantages	Can be carried out on own at times to suit the individual		Intensity can be varied to cater for different ability levels
Sport-related disadvantages	None	Only specific to sports that involve running	None
Equipment-related disadvantages	Benches and bars need to be set up for the person to be able to jump on and off or over	Access to a hill is needed to perform this training	A range of different types of equipment are required
Other disadvantages	Can cause injury as the muscles have to withstand high levels of stress	Requires exercising at very high levels of intensity, which is not appropriate for people with low levels of fitness	

CHECK MY LEARNING

For a sport or activity of your choice, select one fitness training method to improve:

strength   flexibility   power.

Explain your choice, giving the advantages and disadvantages for both the coach and the participant of each method of training selected.

The FITT principles and principles of training (1)

The FITT principles are used to plan training programmes designed to improve fitness of participants and positively affect their participation in sport and activity.

FITT principles

FITT is an acronym for the different principles of training that should be used when designing personal training programmes. The letters stand for the following:

F = Frequency: The number of training sessions completed over a period of time, usually per week

I = Intensity: How hard an individual will train; this is usually expressed as a percentage of maximum intensity

T =Type: The exercise and training method the person takes part in to improve a specific component of fitness

T = Time: How long an individual will train for at each session

So essentially the FITT principles are getting people to think of the following when they are devising a training programme:
- How often?
- How hard?
- What type of training?
- How long?

Application of the FITT principles

Which components of fitness are being trained will determine how the FITT principles are applied to a training programme.

Frequency

The main factor to take into account when applying frequency is to ensure progression and overload are included so that there is a gradual increase in stress placed upon the body. The body will respond by adapting to this training so that cardiovascular fitness and/or musculoskeletal fitness will improve depending on the type of training undertaken.

A person's current fitness levels will have a significant impact on the frequency of training in a training programme. A person with low levels of fitness who is just starting a fitness training programme will only train a few days a week. This is to avoid overloading the body and producing excess strain before it has adapted to cope with the demands of exercise, as this could lead to injuries related to overuse. As a person's fitness levels increase, their body adapts to help them to train more frequently, which results in increasing fitness levels and a greater ability to take part in more frequent training sessions.

Intensity

It is important to exercise at the right intensity so that the training is targeting the right component of fitness, and also to ensure it is of an intensity that will lead to adaptations. Ways to measure intensity are used to help people ensure they are working at the right intensity for each activity.

Rating of perceived exertion (RPE)

The RPE scale can be used as a measure of exercise intensity. The scale ranges from 6 (rest) to 20 (exhaustion).

The person exercising is shown the scale and indicates the number that best represents how hard they feel they are working. The number indicated on the scale can be multiplied by 10 to get an estimate of the person's heart rate during the workout.

RPE × 10 = HR (bpm)

If an individual was working at level 14 on the RPE scale, their heart rate would be calculated as: 14 × 10 = 140 bpm

Percentage of maximum heart rate

For some types of activity, a person should exercise so that their heart is beating at a percentage range of their maximum heart rate so that they are working at the right intensity. Maximum heart rate is worked out using the following equation:

maximum heart rate = 220 − age

Rating of perceived exertion	Intensity
6	No exertion at all
7	Extremely light
8	
9	Very light
10	
11	
12	
13	Somewhat hard
14	
15	Hard (heavy)
16	
17	Very hard
18	
19	Extremely hard
20	Maximal exertion

◘ Figure 2.10: The RPE scale can be used to measure how intensely someone is exercising

---

ACTIVITY

- Work out your maximum heart rate.
- Identify what happens to maximum heart rate as a person gets older.
- Explain why you think this change in maximum heart rate occurs as a person gets older.

Measuring heart rate

There are a variety of ways to measure heart rate; some require technology while some just require access to a clock or stopwatch. The use of technology to measure heart rate provides more accurate and much more detailed heart rate measurements for different phases of training.

Radial and carotid pulse

When the heart beats, it pushes blood through the arteries and these blood vessels respond by expanding when blood is being pushed through them. Then the blood vessels return to their usual size when the heart is relaxed. A pulse point is where an artery can easily be felt passing close to the skin's surface. Pressing on this point slightly closes the blood vessel and each time the heart beats it pushes blood through this vessel; this can be felt as a pulse when applying pressure with fingers to the pulse point.

Use of technology to measure heart rate

The following technology can be used to measure heart rate: apps (applications), smartwatches and heart-rate monitors.

A heart-rate monitor consists of a strap with measuring technology which is usually worn underneath clothing around the chest to 1) measure the heart rate and then 2) record the readings. This is the most accurate method of measuring heart rate. Smartwatches are worn around the wrist, where they measure and record the heart rate data.

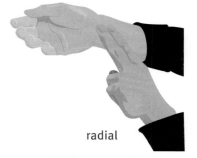
radial

carotid

◘ Figure 2.11: The radial pulse is felt at the wrist and the carotid pulse felt at the neck

---

CHECK MY LEARNING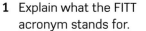

1 Explain what the FITT acronym stands for.

2 Assess the different methods that can be used to measure exercise intensity.

The FITT principles and principles of training (2)

GETTING STARTED

With a partner, discuss the different types of training that you have taken part in and what you have enjoyed and not enjoyed. Compare the sorts of things that can be done to add variety to training, such as using different types of equipment and technology to make it more interesting.

Application of the FITT principles

Type

The type of training used in a training programme will be determined by the component of fitness a participant wants to develop and the method of training participants choose to work on. Different methods of training are used to help to prevent tedium. For example, if a person wanted to improve their aerobic endurance, running the same route for 30 minutes four times a week would soon become very tedious and may stop the person from wanting to take part in the training. Therefore, different types of activities should be included in a training programme, such as gym-based activities, outdoor fitness activities and sport-specific activities.

As an example, a person wishing to improve their cycling performance could vary their training by taking part in:

- outdoor cycling
- cycling on a stationary exercise bike in the gym
- a spinning group exercise class
- mountain biking.

◻ **A spinning class could be an alternative training method for a cyclist.**

Time

The time spent taking part in a training session should be of an appropriate length so that it will encourage progressive overload and be appropriate to the type of training.

For example:
- high intensity, short-duration activities (HIIT training) will usually only last 30 minutes
- training to develop aerobic endurance which includes cardiovascular activities should last at least 20 minutes
- a person who wishes to lose body fat should take part in fat-burning activities that last over 28 minutes
- strength and endurance training time frames are based on sets and reps for each muscle group.

ACTIVITY

For the following participants, identify the time that they should spend training and also the type of training they should take part in, in order to help achieve their training goals.

◻ Table 2.21: Recommendations for training types and times

Participant	Type of training	Time spent training
Chris is overweight and wants to lose excess body fat.		
Anya wants to increase her muscular endurance for rowing.		
Kevin wants to improve his muscle strength for boxing.		
Raj wants to increase his aerobic endurance for cycling.		

CHECK MY LEARNING

For a component of fitness of your choice, write a one-week training programme which applies the FITT principles.

Explain how each FITT principle has been applied and how it would help to develop the named component of fitness.

The FITT principles and principles of training (3)

Application of the principles of training

In addition to the FITT principles, the principles of training provide additional key factors that should be taken into account when designing a training programme to help to improve fitness for sport and activity.

■ Figure 2.12: Principles of training

Specificity

Specificity refers to choosing a training method that aims to improve a specific component of fitness that is beneficial to a particular sport or activity.

Training should be specific because any fitness gain will be specific to the body systems or muscles trained. As different types of training will produce different results, it is important to make sure that your training is specific to the sport that you are competing in. For example, if you are training for a long-distance bike ride you would need to have lots of distance cycling in your training programme. Your cycling performance would not improve if your training only included swimming!

The occasional exercise that is not specific to the sport or activity can also be included in a training programme for variation and to prevent tedium. This training may help to develop other components of fitness which are beneficial for all-round sport and activity participation, such as yoga, which develops flexibility.

Progressive overload

So that fitness gains are continually made, the fitness training programme should progressively overload the muscles or body systems that are being trained. Overload means that the person has to work at a higher intensity than they used to earlier on in the training programme, as their body will have adapted to the training, so doing the same exercise becomes easier.

This continued increase in intensity (how hard a person has to exercise) over a period of time is called progressive overload. This is because, in order to make continued fitness gains, training needs to be demanding enough to cause the body to adapt in order to improve performance.

Overtraining

It is important to be aware of overtraining, when there may be a risk of injury due to fatigue caused by increasing a training workload too quickly.

Overtraining can occur if there is a rapid increase in volume or intensity to the programme or a sudden change in the type of training. Overtraining can also occur if a participant trains when they are experiencing excessive fatigue or if the person has inadequate rest time between each training session.

Reversibility

Reversibility occurs when participants are unable to train. They experience a decrease in fitness and need to restart their training programme at an appropriate level and have some time away from their sport or activity.

The well-known saying associated with this principle of training is 'use it or lose it'. This means that if training stops, or if the intensity of training is not sufficient to cause adaptation, then the training effects are reversed and the body will return to its previous fitness level.

Participant differences and needs

A training programme should be designed to meet a person's specific training goals and also their needs. Participant differences and needs refers to choosing a component of fitness based on fitness data which have been compiled from tests to find out what needs to be focused on in order to help improve performance in a particular sport or activity.

These needs are also determined from the personal goals and competition schedule of the individual. The training programme should include different exercises, types of training, activities and timings to prevent the individual from becoming bored.

Training zones

A training zone is the correct intensity at which a person should exercise in order to experience fitness improvement. Training zones can be used to work out if the training is effective for the targeted component of fitness. Training zones are given as the range of heart rate values an individual should work within in order for training intensity to result in effective fitness improvement.

◘ Table 2.22: Training zones and their heart rate values

Training zone	Percentage of maximal heart rate
Maintenance of fitness levels and warm-up	50–60
Fat-burning zone	60–70
Aerobic training zone	70–80
Anaerobic training zone	80–100

Alternatively, RPE can be used to measure the intensity of the exercise.

ACTIVITY

Work out your maximum heart rate (220 minus age).

Then work out your heart rate for the following zones:
- maintenance of fitness levels and warm-up
- fat-burning zone
- aerobic training zone
- anaerobic training.

CHECK MY LEARNING

Identify each of the principles of training and give examples of how you could, or already do, implement these in a training programme.

Understanding fitness programmes (1)

GETTING STARTED

In a small group, discuss the reasons why you think people take part in training programmes. Consider a range of different people, from those that have never really taken part in a training programme to elite performers. Make a list of reasons and share your list with the rest of the class. Explain if there are any trends in the reasons that the class come up with.

When designing a fitness programme, you should follow a specific structure which contains key information to help improve fitness for an individual and improve their performance in sport and activity.

The key information that should be included in addition to the FITT principles and principles of training are:

- person-centred approach
- aims
- objectives
- selection of appropriate components of fitness for training
- safe design
- components of a participant's session plan.

Person-centred approach

To help ensure the fitness training programme is appropriate and safe for a participant, it is important to gather information about them so that it is designed to fully meet their needs.

Initially, a health-screening questionnaire should be completed to ensure it is safe for the participant to take part in a training programme. A PAR-Q is a popular health screening questionnaire used in many health centres. It is used to identify if a person has incidences of heart-related problems, lung conditions such as asthma, or long-term injuries that may affect their ability to take part in sport or physical activity.

QUESTION	YES	NO
1. Has your doctor ever said you have heart trouble? If yes, please state:		
2. Do you frequently have pains in your heart and chest? If yes, please state:		
3. Do you often feel faint or have spells of severe dizziness? If yes, please state:		
4. Has a doctor ever said your blood pressure was too high? If yes, please state:		
5. Has your doctor ever told you that you have a bone or joint problem(s), such as arthritis, that has been aggravated by exercise, or might be made worse with exercise? If yes, please state:		
6. Is there a good physical reason, not mentioned here, why you should not follow an activity programme even if you wanted to? If yes, please state:		
7. Are you or have you been pregnant in the last 6 months?		
8. Do you suffer from any problems of the lower back, i.e. chronic pain or numbness? If yes, please state:		
9. Are you currently taking any medications? If YES, please specify.		
10. Do you currently have a disability or a communicable disease? If yes, please state:		

If you answered NO to all questions above, it gives a general indication that you may participate in physical activities. The fact that you answered NO to the above questions is no guarantee that you will have a normal response to exercise. If you answered Yes to any of the above questions, consult with your doctor as to your suitability to take part in physical activities.

Print name ____________ Signature ____________ Date ____________

Figure 2.13: An example of a PAR-Q

Select four questions from the PAR-Q and explain why you think it is important that a person declares this information before they take part in physical activities.

Lifestyle questionnaire

A lifestyle questionnaire provides an overview of a person's lifestyle and asks questions related to their occupation, their diet and if they drink alcohol or smoke. It can also be used to find out the person's likes and dislikes, as well as how much time and availability they have to exercise.

Figure 2.14 shows an example of some questions on a lifestyle questionnaire.

1) Do you smoke?   YES   NO
   If yes, how many per day?   _____

2) Do you drink alcohol?   YES   NO
   If yes, how many units per week? _____

3) How many hours do you regularly sleep at night?   _____

4) What is your occupation?   _____

5) How many hours a day do you work?

6) Describe your activity levels:
   ☐ Sedentary
   ☐ Lightly active
   ☐ Moderately active
   ☐ Very active

7) What types of physical activities do you like to take part in?

8) What types of physical activities do you dislike?

■ Figure 2.14: Example of a lifestyle questionnaire

Write three or four more questions that could be added to the lifestyle questionnaire to provide more information on a person's likes and dislikes as well as their availability to exercise.

1 List the key information that should be included in a fitness training programme.
2 Explain why a PAR-Q and lifestyle questionnaire should be used to help ensure a person-centred approach when designing a fitness training programme.

Understanding fitness programmes (2)

It is important that you are able to understand the structure of fitness training programmes. This will help you to understand how they can be developed and used for an individual to help to improve their targeted fitness requirements.

Aims

An aim is something the participant hopes to achieve. In the context of fitness, the overall aim for the training programme should meet the participant's main fitness, sport or activity goal.

- **An example of an aim** could be for a participant to be able to run at a higher intensity for a longer period of time in order to complete a half marathon race in a specific time.

Objectives

An objective is a statement of intent of how the participant will achieve their aim, i.e. the steps they will need to take to reach their main goal.

- **An example of an objective** may be for a participant to complete three aerobic endurance training sessions that last for at least 30 minutes per week to help a person achieve their overall aim of completing a 5 km fun run.

Selection of appropriate components of fitness for training

Components of fitness that you will need to consider in a training programme are:
- flexibility
- strength
- muscular endurance
- power
- aerobic endurance
- speed.

Training methods for each of these components of fitness are included in this book. For some components of fitness there are a range of different training methods. In some cases one training method may be better for the participant or their sport compared to another method to train the same component of fitness. In other cases, a combination of each training method for the specific component of fitness may be beneficial to have in an individual's training programme.

ACTIVITY

Draw images that will help you to remember the components of fitness that can be focused on in a training programme. State the component of fitness each image represents.

For example, for flexibility you could draw a person performing the splits.

Safe design

Appropriate training methods and activities should be chosen to ensure the programme is training the targeted component of fitness. The training and activities should also be appropriate to the fitness level of the person: for example, a beginner who wants to improve their power would not go straight into plyometric training, jumping off benches, as their muscular system would not be strong enough to cope with the impact and it may result in injury. Instead, hill sprints would be more appropriate so that they can go at their own pace and work at an intensity that suits their individual needs and ability.

Components of a participant's session plan

To recap, there are key components that should be included in a participant's session plan. These include:
- warm-up – at the start of the session a warm-up needs to be in place to increase the heart rate and increase the mobility of the joints to get the body ready for participation in exercise
- main activities – specific training methods need to be included in the main part of the activity session that are appropriate to train the targeted components of fitness, in order to meet the participant's main fitness goal
- cool down – after the main activities, a cool down needs to be in place to gradually decrease the heart rate to return it to pre-exercise levels. The cool down will also encourage the removal of waste products such as lactic acid. This all helps to reduce the feelings of muscle soreness after training.

CHECK MY LEARNING

Think of a fitness improvement that you would like to make. Complete the following information to help design a structure for a training programme to meet your fitness improvement goal.
- Aims.
- Objectives.
- Identify the component(s) of fitness that will need to be trained.
- Describe the training methods that you could use to train the identified components of fitness.
- Describe activities that you would include in the warm-up, main activities and cool down for an exercise session in your training programme.

Learning aim A: assessment practice

How you will be assessed

All of this component is assessed through a written assessment which is set and marked by Pearson.

The written external assessment will contain short and extended questions which cover each learning aim in the component.

For this learning aim you will need to demonstrate knowledge of the principles of training and an understanding of how training can improve fitness. You will also need to be able to analyse and evaluate data and information related to fitness.

CHECKPOINT

Strengthen
- Be able to understand fitness test scores.
- Be able to compare fitness test scores to normative data for different target groups.
- Know how to select training methods to improve specific components of fitness.
- Know the advantages and disadvantages of different fitness training methods.
- Know the FITT principles and principles of training and how they are used to improve fitness.
- Understand the structure of a fitness training programme.

Challenge
- Understand how a fitness test score impacts on a person's ability to take part in sport and activity.
- Be able to recommend different types of training for specific participant needs.
- Be able to use the FITT principles and principles of training to improve targeted components of fitness for participants taking part in specific sports and activities.

ASSESSMENT ACTIVITY — LEARNING AIM A

Review the fitness test results for Ronnie, a 19-year-old female.

☐ **Table 2.23: Fitness test results for a 19-year-old female**

Test	Result	Result/category
Cooper 12-minute run	2500 m	
Hand grip dynamometer	22	
One-minute sit-up	18	
Sit and reach	35 cm	
Sergeant jump	22 m	
30-metre sprint	5 seconds	

Use normative data tables to interpret the fitness test results.

1 a) Identify two tests that Ronnie scored poorly in. (2 marks)

   b) Identify the component of fitness tested by the sit and reach test. (1 mark)

   c) State two training methods that could be used to develop the component of fitness tested by the sit and reach test. (2 marks)

2 Teddy takes part in cross-country running races.

   Table 2.24 shows Teddy's training programme.

   Duration of each session 40 minutes

   Activities in the session Continuous training and fartlek training

   Number of times a week training sessions are carried out 4

   Percentage of maximal heart rate 70-80%

   a) Identify how each of the FITT principles have been applied in this training programme. (4 marks)

   b) Explain why fartlek training may be a more appropriate training method for a cross-country runner compared to continuous training. (2 marks)

TIPS

You may like to review different training programmes to see how they are written and take into account the FITT principles, principles of training and the structure of a training programme. You or a person in your class may be following a training programme, so use this information to help you to see how they are set out and developed on a weekly basis.

TAKE IT FURTHER

Select a specific sport or activity for the person who you are writing a training programme for from the choices below:

basketball   200 m running   volleyball   tennis.

Ensure the training methods and programme are specific to the selected sport or activity and provide advantages and disadvantages of the programme related to the participant's selected sport or activity.

Nutrition for sport and activity

 Eating healthy foods can have a significant impact on health and well-being.

The food and fluids we choose to consume are very important as they have a significant impact on our health and well-being. In addition, specific quantities and types of food and fluid intake can help to improve sporting performance. It is therefore important to know about nutrition, so we are able to eat the right kinds of foods in the correct quantities to help us to reach our sport and activity-related goals.

Nutrients can be divided into two main groups; **macronutrients** and **micronutrients**.

Macronutrients

Macronutrients are needed in large amounts in the diet and provide energy for the body. They are also used to help to build the structures of the body and carry out functions that are needed to sustain life.

There are three macronutrients:

- carbohydrates
- protein
- fats.

KEY TERMS

Macro means large. Macronutrients should be eaten in large quantities.

Micro means small. Micronutrients should be eaten in small quantities.

Macronutrients are nutrients that are needed in large amounts and contain energy.

Micronutrients are needed in smaller amounts and contain no energy.

ACTIVITY

Make a list of foods that you think contain high quantities of:
- carbohydrates
- protein
- fat.

Micronutrients

These are substances that the body requires in very small amounts and are called vitamins and minerals. The body is incapable of making vitamins and minerals for its overall needs, so they must be supplied regularly by the diet. As vitamins were discovered, each was identified by a letter; as more were discovered, some were also given a number, e.g. B1. Many of the vitamins with the same letter consist of several closely related compounds which provide similar functions in the body.

ACTIVITY

- Make a list of all the vitamins that you have heard of.
- Make a list of all the minerals that you have heard of.
- Identify reasons why you think each of the vitamins and minerals that you have identified should be consumed.

Calories

A **calorie** is a measurement of the energy available in food and drink. The more calories a food or drink has, the more energy it will provide. A recommended daily allowance (RDA) of calories is worked out for males and females to have sufficient energy to carry out their everyday activities. As men are generally larger than females, the RDA is higher for men than women as it takes more energy for a larger person to move themselves around compared to a smaller person.

KEY TERM

A **calorie** is a measurement of the amount of energy in an item of food or drink.

■ Table 2.25: RDAs for men and women

	Men	Women
Recommended daily allowance of calories (kcal)	2500	2000

However, the more sport and/or activity a person does, the more calories they will need on a daily basis so that they have sufficient energy to participate in the selected sport or activity.

If a person consumes more calories than they need, the excess will be turned into fat and stored in the body.

CHECK MY LEARNING

Make a list of the foods and fluids that you consumed yesterday.

Next to each food, write down which macronutrients it mainly contained and if any micronutrients were present. Where possible, try to include if the food was complex or simple carbohydrate and unsaturated or saturated fat.

Assess your food intake and work out if you have eaten a range of macronutrients and micronutrients, or if there are some that you have eaten too much or too little of.

Macronutrients – carbohydrates

Carbohydrates should provide around 50–60 per cent of the daily calorie intake. Different countries will often have a preferred form of carbohydrate in their diet as some types of carbohydrate grow better in different climates. For example, in Asia rice is the main form of carbohydrate, whereas bread and potatoes provide the main form of carbohydrate in the UK.

Structure

Carbohydrates come in two main forms: simple carbohydrates and complex carbohydrates. Fibre is also a nutrient that is a form of carbohydrate.

Simple carbohydrates

These carbohydrates are called simple as they only consist of one molecule. As they are only made up of one molecule they are quickly digested by the body and provide energy very quickly. These types of carbohydrates taste sweet.

Complex carbohydrates

These carbohydrates are called complex as they are made up of many molecules that are joined together. To release the energy from a complex carbohydrate, the joins between the molecules need to be broken down, which takes time. This means that these types of carbohydrates provide a slow release of energy. These types of carbohydrates do not taste sweet.

Excess carbohydrates in the diet will be converted to and stored as fat. Eating excess carbohydrates can lead to health problems such as diabetes, obesity and coronary heart disease.

Fibre

Fibre is a carbohydrate and contains calories; however, our digestive system is not able to use these calories. Instead, fibre moves through the digestive system and is then excreted. The main function of fibre is to help prevent constipation and haemorrhoids because when it moves through the digestive system it helps to retain water, which makes the stools easier to pass. Fibre also helps to slow down how quickly the stomach empties and how quickly glucose enters the bloodstream.

◻ Complex carbohydrates provide a slow release of energy.

Function

The main functions of carbohydrates are to:
- provide energy for the brain to function
- provide energy for the liver to perform its functions
- provide energy for muscular contractions at moderate to high intensities.

Sources

 Table 2.26: Sources of carbohydrates and fibre

Simple carbohydrates	Complex carbohydrates	Fibre
Fruit	Pasta	Wholegrain breakfast cereal
Chocolate	Rice	Whole wheat pasta
Sweets	Potatoes	Wholegrain bread
Glucose drink	Oats	Oats
	Bread	Vegetables

ACTIVITY

The following are sources of simple and complex carbohydrates and fibre. Identify which ones are simple carbohydrates, complex carbohydrates and/or fibre.
- orange
- carrot
- porridge
- wholegrain breakfast cereal
- spaghetti
- sports energy drink
- jelly beans
- boiled potatoes
- granary bread
- peas
- strawberry jam
- muesli with raisins
- ravioli.

CHECK MY LEARNING

1 Make a list of all foods that you have eaten today or yesterday.
2 Next to each, identify which ones are simple carbohydrates, complex carbohydrates and/or fibre.
3 Explain if you think you are eating enough carbohydrates in your diet.

Macronutrients – protein

GETTING STARTED

The following foods contain high levels of protein: red meat, chicken, fish, eggs, milk and beans.

Discuss with a partner any trends in the types of foods that contain high levels of protein. Discuss if there are any types of diets in which people may struggle to consume sufficient quantities of protein, with reasons for each.

Protein is a word that comes from Greek and means primary or holding first place. Proteins in nutrition are very important in the diet as they are used to make the structure of our body. The diet should consist of between 12 to 15 per cent of protein depending on the specific needs of the individual.

Structure

The smallest unit of a protein is called an amino acid and there are 20 amino acids in total. Proteins are made up of different combinations of amino acids. If you imagine amino acids are like the alphabet, we have 26 letters in the English alphabet which can make millions of words. The amino acid alphabet contains 20 amino acids, and from these, approximately 50,000 different proteins can be made and are present in the body.

The 20 different amino acids can be split into two categories: essential and non-essential amino acids.
- There are 9 essential amino acids – an essential amino acid is one which we must eat.
- There are 11 non-essential amino acids – a non-essential amino acid can be made in the body by the liver if the liver has access to all the essential amino acids.

This means that, for the body to be able to grow and repair appropriately, we must eat all of the essential amino acids on a daily basis.

ACTIVITY

Foods which contain all nine essential amino acids are described as being complete, while a food which is missing one or more essential amino acids is described as being incomplete.

Table 2.27 shows sources of complete and incomplete proteins.

◘ **Table 2.27 Sources of complete and incomplete proteins**

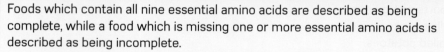

Complete protein	Incomplete protein
Chicken	Wheat
Eggs	Oats
Fish	Rice
Red meat	Pulses
Dairy products (milk, cheese)	Nuts
Soya beans	Vegetables

- Identify which sources of complete protein a **vegetarian** could eat.
- Explain which sources of complete protein a **vegan** could eat.

KEY TERMS
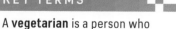

A **vegetarian** is a person who does not eat meat or fish.

A **vegan** is a person who does not eat meat, fish or any foods that come from an animal, such as eggs or milk.

Function

Proteins provide the building blocks which make up the structures of the body; for example, our muscle tissues, skin, bones, internal organs, etc. all contain some protein. Protein is required for growth which is important in developing children. Protein is also needed in children and fully grown adults to repair body tissues on a daily basis. For example, skin cells are continually being produced to replace old and damaged skin. After exercise, protein from the diet is used to repair muscle tissues.

ACTIVITY

Protein is used for growth and repair.
- Explain why you think it is very important for young children and pregnant women to eat sufficient quantities of protein in their diet.
- Explain why a person who takes part in weight training may require higher levels of protein in their diet compared to a person who does not take part in weight training.

Sources

▫ **High protein foods can come from plant and animal sources.**

Protein is mainly found in foods that are from animal origin. However, some plant-based proteins are good sources of protein.
- Animal-based proteins include chicken, turkey, fish and lean beef.
- Plant-based proteins include meat substitutes (such as soya mince), beans, nuts and seeds.

CHECK MY LEARNING

1 Describe the structure of protein.
2 Explain the difference between an essential and non-essential amino acid.
3 List ten food sources that contain protein.

Macronutrients – fats

GETTING STARTED

In small groups, look at the food labels from foods that you have eaten recently or have brought with you that you plan to eat later. From the labels, what do you notice about the fat content of the food?

Is fat labelled as just fat or is it listed as different types of fat? Make a list of what is stated on the packaging.

Describe which types of food contain more fat than others. Explain whether people in your group have preference for some foods that may contain high levels of fat, with reasons for their preferences such as taste or texture.

Fats are often thought of as being bad for you but fat is an essential nutrient in a diet. However, some fats are better for you than others and excess consumption of fats will lead to health problems, often having a negative impact on sporting performance. As fat provides just over twice as much energy per gram as carbohydrates and protein, a diet that contains high levels of fat can mean it is more likely to contain more calories than required, which results in increased stores of body fat.

A person's diet should consist of around 30 per cent fat, with only 10 per cent of that from saturated fats.

Structure

Fats can be either saturated or unsaturated. The terms saturated and unsaturated relate to the chemical structure of the fat.

Saturated

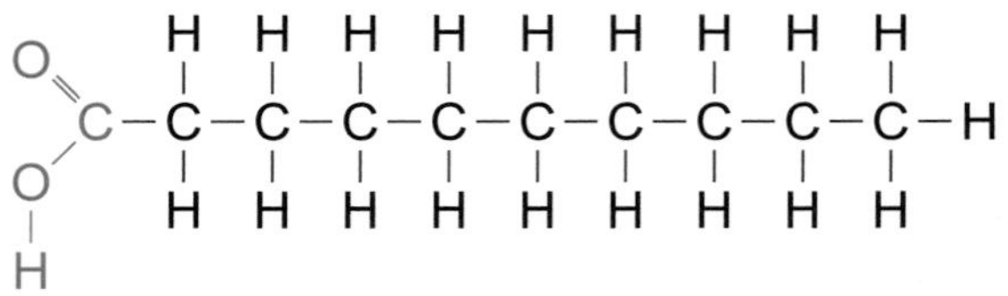

Unsaturated

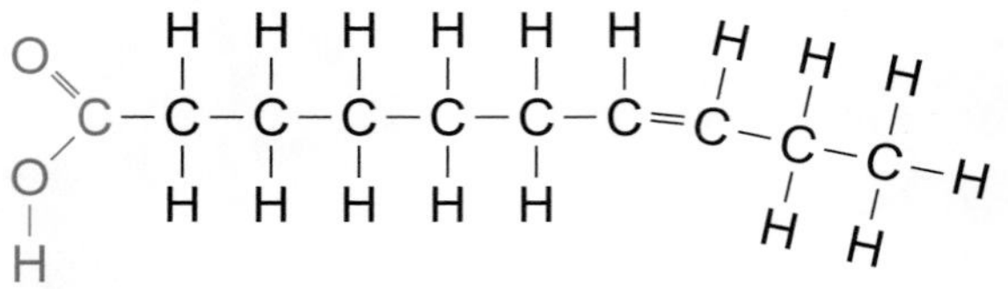

Figure 2.15: The structure of fat will determine if it is saturated or unsaturated

A saturated fat consists of a long chain of carbon atoms. Where all the carbon atoms are attached to hydrogen molecules, the chain is said to be saturated with hydrogen. The carbon atoms each have single bonds between them in the chain and hydrogen atoms are attached to each carbon atom. The majority of saturated fats come from animal sources. The Department of Health recommends a person should have a maximum of 10 per cent of calories coming from saturated fat.

Unsaturated fats have hydrogen atoms missing from the carbon chain causing the carbon atoms to attach to each other with double bonds. This is because carbon has to have four bonds and if there is no hydrogen present the carbon atoms will bond to each other. In this case the carbon chain is not saturated with hydrogen atoms and is therefore 'unsaturated'.

A monounsaturated fat is one where there is just one double bond in the carbon chain and a polyunsaturated fat has many double bonds in the carbon chain. The majority of unsaturated fats come from plant sources.

ACTIVITY

Draw the following structures using the images of saturated and unsaturated fats in Figure 2.15 to support you:
- a saturated fat with 12 carbon atoms in the carbon chain
- an unsaturated fat with 8 carbon atoms in the carbon chain.

Function

Unsaturated fats are used as an energy source for all low to moderate intensity activities such as walking and a slow jog. They are also used to supply energy for simple everyday activities, such as energy for the muscles in the respiratory system to contract so that we can breathe when at rest and for our muscles to contract to allow us to stand up.

Saturated fats increase the total cholesterol in the body. Cholesterol can either be eaten or is made in the body. Cholesterol is only found in animal products, never in plants. It has some useful functions including building cell membranes and helping the function of various hormones. However, too much cholesterol is responsible for a build-up in the lining of the walls of arteries which can lead to an increased risk of coronary heart disease.

Sources

◘ **Table 2.28: Some sources of saturated and unsaturated fats**

Saturated fats	Unsaturated fats
Animal fats such as fat found on red meat	Oily fish (e.g. salmon, mackerel, pilchards)
Dairy products (e.g. milk, cheese, cream)	Pumpkin seeds
	Almonds
	Walnuts
	Avocados

CHECK MY LEARNING

1 Describe the difference between saturated and unsaturated fats.
2 Identify the main food sources of:
- saturated fats and their origin
- unsaturated fats and their origin.
3 Explain if you think vegetarian diets or vegan diets may be a healthier alternative to diets which contain animal products.

Benefits of macronutrients to participation in sport or activity

Participants in some sports and activities will benefit from eating certain types of macronutrients or differing quantities of the macronutrients to help them with their performance. The timing and selection of foods consumed can also have an impact on performance, so it is important for people who regularly take part in sport and activity to be aware of the performance gains they can make from eating the right types of food and drink at the right times.

Carbohydrates

A person would need to be exercising at a moderate to moderately high intensity for them to be using carbohydrates as the main energy source.

Complex carbohydrates

Complex carbohydrates are broken down slowly in the body and provide energy for aerobic activities. As this type of carbohydrate is broken down slowly, energy is released gradually over a long period of time, which means it will continue to supply energy for the duration of most aerobic activities (as these usually last for at least 30 minutes).

Simple carbohydrates

Simple carbohydrates are broken down very quickly in the body, which means they will enter the bloodstream quickly to be taken to the areas of the muscles in the body that are working. They therefore help to provide a boost of energy before a person is about to take part in sport or activity.

They can also be taken during exercise as they are easy to digest and are therefore less likely to cause any stomach upsets compared to macronutrients that take longer to digest. People taking part in sports and activities that last longer than 90 minutes will usually run out of their body's stores of carbohydrates. So it is important to consume simple carbohydrates in these types of sports to continue to allow the body to use carbohydrates as an energy source for muscle contraction and be able to exercise at moderate to moderately high intensity.

After exercise, simple carbohydrates can be consumed to help the person to recover from the sport or activity and to refuel the body's stores of carbohydrate.

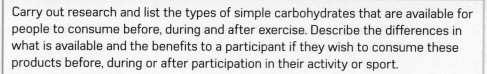

ACTIVITY

Carry out research and list the types of simple carbohydrates that are available for people to consume before, during and after exercise. Describe the differences in what is available and the benefits to a participant if they wish to consume these products before, during or after participation in their activity or sport.

Protein

We know the main function of protein is for growth and repair of body tissue. When taking part in sport and activity, the muscle tissues undergo some very small tears called micro tears. This is all perfectly normal and not a type of sports injury. However, the muscle tissue needs to be repaired and it needs protein to fully repair. When a person takes part in strength training, the focus of training is actually on producing micro tears in the muscle fibres. These micro tears stimulate the muscle tissue to repair and actually grow bigger so that it is more able to cope with the stress of the exercise that the person is taking part in. This means that the muscle tissues that are being exercised get bigger and bigger; these muscles are then able to produce more force which means a person's strength will increase.

Research indicates that consuming protein foods and fluids straight after exercise which has stressed the muscle system helps to repair the muscle tissue at a faster rate than if they are consumed some time after the activity. Protein is very important therefore to help to promote muscle growth, as well as helping to prevent injury which could occur if muscle tissue was not fully repaired after participation in sport or activity (because it would be in a weakened state and potentially more likely to tear).

ACTIVITY

Identify which type of sports injury a person may be more prone to if they do not eat enough protein in their diet after having taken part in strength training exercise. Provide some reasons for your choice of sports injury.

Fats

Fat stored in the body can be broken down to supply energy for muscle contraction, so it acts as a second energy source to the main energy source, which is the body's store of carbohydrates or any carbohydrates that are consumed when exercising.

However, fat does not produce energy at the same rate as carbohydrates. So if a person is using fat as their only energy source they will not be able to exercise at a high to moderate intensity. For instance, if running, they would only be able to move at the pace of a slow jog if fat was the only energy source. What happens is that fat is used as a back-up energy source and will supply low levels of energy during low intensity exercise periods. For example, if a netball player is walking back to their position after a goal is scored, fat will be supplying the energy to do this. However, when the netball player sprints out to receive the centre throw, they will be using carbohydrates to supply the energy for their high intensity sprint.

CHECK MY LEARNING

1 Explain why complex carbohydrates are a good source of carbohydrate for people who take part in aerobic activities.

2 Explain why a body builder should have sufficient levels of protein in their diet.

3 Describe how fat can be used as a second energy source.

Micronutrients – vitamins and minerals

There are many different types of vitamins and minerals; some are needed for everyday health and also have an impact on sports performance. Tables 2.29 and 2.30 list the vitamins and minerals that you will need to learn.

Each vitamin and mineral has a specific function in relation to why it is needed by the body. If insufficient quantities of the micronutrient are eaten then this would lead to varying degrees of the function not being able to be carried out. The sources provided are some of the main sources of each vitamin and mineral; other foods are good sources too.

Vitamins

▣ Table 2.29: The functions and sources of vitamins A, B1, C and D

Vitamin	Function	Sources
A	Maintains normal eyesight to assist hand–eye coordination and positional awareness	liver, mackerel and milk products
B1	Converts food into energy to produce energy for exercise	rice, bran, pork, beef, peas, beans, soya beans
C	Maintains an effective immune system to prevent illness so the performer can train on a regular basis	most fresh fruit and vegetables
D	Keeps bones, teeth and muscles healthy	oily fish, red meat, liver, egg yolks, **fortified foods**

Vitamins B1 and C are water-soluble vitamins which means they cannot be stored in the body and therefore should be consumed on a regular basis. If a person were to eat more of these vitamins than needed, the excess is excreted in urine.

Vitamins A and D are fat-soluble vitamins which means they are stored in the body's fat tissue. This means it is not necessary to consume foods which contain these vitamins on such a regular basis. It is unusual but possible to overdose on fat-soluble vitamins if too much is consumed, which can be detrimental to health.

Minerals

▣ Table 2.30: The functions and sources of potassium, iron and calcium

Mineral	Function	Sources
Potassium	Regulates body fluid levels to help ensure a person is hydrated during exercise	bananas, yoghurt, sunflower seeds, potatoes
Iron	Increases the body's oxygen-carrying capacity to enhance aerobic performance by delivering oxygen to working muscles	liver, lean meat, eggs, kidney beans, spinach
Calcium	Provides increased bone strength, which reduces the risk of injury in contact activities	milk and dairy products, whole grains, green vegetables

Benefits of micronutrients to performance in sport and activity

Micronutrients are beneficial to sporting performance. Consuming too many micronutrients can be detrimental to health and therefore could decrease sporting performance.

Vitamin A

This vitamin helps to keep the eyes healthy and maintain good vision. This is required in sports where good **hand–eye coordination** is needed, for example in racket sports such as tennis and badminton.

The eyes are also needed to provide information to the brain about the **positional awareness** of the person. This is used in virtually all sports so that a person can work out where they are and make decisions to help them perform their sport or activity.

Vitamin B

The B group vitamins, which includes vitamin B1, are not chemically related, but often occur in the same types of foods. Their main function is to aid in the breakdown of food to convert it into energy which is needed for muscle contraction. Therefore, all participants in sport and activity will require this vitamin to ensure they are able to turn the food that they have consumed into usable energy.

Vitamin C

Vitamin C can help to prevent a person from getting ill as it helps to fight bacterial infections. If a person is unwell they are not able to train, so fitness gains from training are lost. Vitamin C allows participants to train and become fitter and also play more often. In turn, this will improve skills and techniques in that sport or activity and therefore help to increase their performance.

Potassium

Potassium helps to maintain fluid and electrolyte balance in the body. Around 60 per cent of our body is made up of water. We also have electrolytes in our body fluids which are chemicals that help all body functions such as muscle contraction. It is important that a balance of fluids and electrolytes in the body is maintained, as in sport and during activity fluids and electrolytes are lost in sweat when the body is regulating its temperature by trying to cool down. We also do this by drinking fluids and consuming fluid-containing foods. Also, fluids are excreted regularly to remove waste matter.

Iron

Iron is needed by the body to produce red blood cells. Red blood cells carry oxygen around the body and to the muscles which is then used to produce energy for muscle contraction. Red blood cells need to be continually produced as they only last in the body for around 100–120 days. By ensuring sufficient iron is consumed it will enhance aerobic performance as it promotes the growth of red blood cells.

Calcium

Bones are continually being broken down and new bone is formed. In this process, calcium is used to help to increase the strength of bones. This mineral therefore helps to reduce the risk of bone-related injuries, such as fractures.

KEY TERMS

Hand–eye coordination means the control of hand movements using visual input to guide the movements of the hand.

Positional awareness is the awareness of the physical position in which a person is located.

CHECK MY LEARNING

For a sport or activity of your choice:
- identify foods that contain key vitamins and minerals that would be beneficial to your performance
- explain how each vitamin and mineral would be beneficial for your performance.

Hydration

GETTING STARTED

Sports drinks are very popular and there are lots of different brands to choose from.

Make a list of all the different types of sports drinks that you have consumed or seen. Explain why you think many people are choosing sports drinks to rehydrate after or during sport or activity rather than water.

It is possible to survive for a number of weeks without food as the body stores energy in the form of body fat. However, the body does not store any water. As such, a person would only be able to survive for around three days without drinking any water.

We lose approximately 2 litres of water every day through breathing, sweating and urine production. Taking part in sport or activity increases the amount of water lost as sweat is produced as a method of cooling down the body. Additional fluid intake is recommended if you are taking part in sports and activities.

DID YOU KNOW?

When we breathe out, water is lost from our body. This can be seen from breathing onto a window and making it 'steam up' from the water that is breathed out.

Dehydration

Dehydration is a harmful reduction in the amount of fluid in the body. It occurs when fluid loss exceeds fluid intake. The signs and symptoms of dehydration are:

- thirst
- dizziness
- headaches
- dry mouth
- poor concentration
- rapid heart rate.

DID YOU KNOW?

It is possible to determine hydration levels from the colour of urine excreted by the body – the darker the colour, the more concentrated the urine and the less hydrated a person is. Conversely, the lighter the colour the more hydrated they are.

1, 2, 3 Well hydrated	1
	2
	3
4, 5 Hydrated, but not well hydrated	4
	5
6, 7, 8 Dehydrated – You need to drink more	6
	7
	8

Figure 2.16: It is possible to tell how well hydrated someone is from the colour of their urine

We are not very good at detecting when we are dehydrated. When you start to feel thirsty you will have already lost around 2% of your body water content so will be in the first stages of dehydration. It is therefore important to drink hydrating fluids regularly to ensure you are fully hydrated.

Recommended daily intake (RDI)

It is recommended that a person has two litres of fluid per day. This intake should be increased if a person takes part in sport and activity, with one additional litre of fluid per hour of exercise participation. If the environment is hot then this RDI and additional amounts consumed when taking part in exercise should be increased even further, as more fluid will be lost through sweating.

We know that fluid is found in drinks but it is also present in foods such as fruit. So it is not always necessary to drink the full two litres per day if foods high in water are also consumed as part of your dietary intake.

Consequences of poor hydration

If a person does not consume sufficient fluids or has poor fluid choices, which means drinking fluids that are not good at hydrating a person, then it can lead to dehydration. When this happens it will cause a loss of blood plasma which reduces the volume of blood and the blood actually gets thicker. Sweat is produced, mainly from fluid from blood plasma, so when there is less blood plasma, less sweat can be produced. This will then result in body temperature increasing as the person cannot lose excess body heat from sweating. This results in dehydration, causing a significant loss of performance.

Some fluids can actually have a dehydrating effect on the body. Drinks that contain caffeine, such as coffee and cola drinks, are not good choices to rehydrate the body. Also, drinks that are high in sugar such as lemonade or energy drinks with high levels of sugar are not good choices for rehydration. Any drinks that contain alcohol, such as beer or cider, will have a dehydrating effect on the body.

CHECK MY LEARNING

1 Describe what is meant by dehydration.

2 Identify the RDI of fluid:
   - when not exercising
   - when a person is participating in exercise.

3 Explain which types of drinks should be avoided when trying to rehydrate after taking part in exercise.

Benefits of hydration for sport and activity

Being fully hydrated is not only beneficial for general health and well-being, it is also very beneficial for maximising performance in sport and activity.

◘ It is important to be able to rehydrate while you are on the move.

Maintaining a normal body temperature

Your skin temperature can vary a great deal but your core temperature has to remain at 37°C, as an increase or decrease of 1°C or more will affect a person's physical and mental health and sports performance. When exercising, the contraction of muscles produces heat energy, so the body has to cool itself down to maintain a core temperature of 37°C. Evaporation of sweat from the body is the major method of heat loss in people. As the sweat evaporates from the skin surface it has a cooling effect on the blood passing through the blood vessels that are close to the skin's surface. So that a person can lose as much heat as possible from evaporation, they need to produce high levels of sweat and therefore must be fully hydrated and also have normal levels of salt and electrolytes in their body.

Lubrication for the joints

A joint is where two or more bones meet. When we move, the bones in the joints need to be able to move past each other smoothly to prevent any damage to the bones and the joint area. If this smooth movement does not happen, it could lead to discomfort or injury in the joint area. To help the joints of the body to move freely, a fluid called synovial fluid is located in a capsule that surrounds the joint area. Water in the body is used to produce synovial fluid, so if a person is dehydrated there would be less fluid in the joint which could lead to a reduced range of movement around the joint or damage to the joint area.

Blood plasma is thinner

Blood plasma makes up around 55 per cent of the body's total blood volume and is mainly made up of water. It is a watery solution that holds the different components of blood such as red blood cells and white blood cells, as well as transporting nutrients, hormones and proteins around the body. Water from blood plasma provides the sweat glands with the fluid they need to produce sweat. When a person is fully hydrated the blood plasma is less concentrated so it is thinner and able to travel more readily through the blood vessels around the body. This makes it work more effectively in transporting oxygen around the body to the working muscles during sport and activity.

ACTIVITY

Carry out research to find out about three different types of sports drinks that are available.

For each drink, identify:
- the name
- the ingredients
- the beneficial products the drink contains to support sporting performance
- the cost.

Evaluate which drink you think would be most effective for you to consume when taking part in a sport of your choice, giving reasons for your choice.

CHECK MY LEARNING

1 Explain the role of fluids in maintaining body temperature.
2 Assess why hydration is important to help ensure a person can move their joints to their full range of movement.
3 Explain why dehydration can have a negative effect on performance in aerobic sports or activities.

Improving nutrition for sport and activity

GETTING STARTED

Review your diet by making a list of everything that you can remember eating and drinking yesterday. Assess the types of foods that you ate and write a paragraph to explain if you think you have eaten sufficient quantities of macronutrients and micronutrients or, if you haven't, how your diet could be improved. Explain if you think you have drunk sufficient fluids or if you should increase the amount of fluids you drink, with reasons why this would be beneficial.

Features of a healthy diet

A healthy diet is important to maintain optimal health and well-being. To ensure we are all eating a healthy diet there are some key features we should follow:.

1 Eating the right amount of each macronutrient is important – recommended percentages are shown in Table 2.31.

■ Table 2.31: Recommended percentage intake of macronutrients in a healthy diet

Macronutrient	Carbohydrates	Fat	Protein
Percentage intake to stay healthy	50–60%	30%	12–15%

The diet should include the correct quantities of vitamins and minerals to help ensure the body is able to function as well as possible.

2 Good hydration levels are important to ensure we stay fully hydrated.

3 Eating at least three meals a day is important to ensure blood sugar levels remain constant. Low levels of blood sugar can lead to lethargy and an inability to concentrate. Eating at regular intervals helps to prevent this dip in blood sugar levels.

4 Exploring ways to improve and enhance the diet is a good idea. For example, if a person realises they are not eating enough protein they can explore how to include foods that contain high levels of protein in their diet, such as snacking on nuts or having scrambled eggs for breakfast.

5 There are many different types of foods available and a range of methods of preparing food which can be beneficial to health and increase the nutritional value of foods. It is therefore always a good idea to try new foods and have variety in the diet, as well as experiment with different methods of food preparation.

Recognising features of a healthy diet

To help you to recognise features of a healthy diet, here are some guidelines on what sorts of things to look out for.

1 Choose foods which are naturally occurring rather than processed. A processed food is one that has been changed in some way from the way it has been prepared. For example, bacon is processed by soaking it in a salt solution. However, a pork chop has not been through any food processing and is therefore a more healthy choice. If foods are selected that look the same as they would when they occur in nature, this would indicate they have not been altered in any way through processing.

◨ Food in its natural form, such as a potato, is a healthier choice than crisps, which are a type of processed food made from potato.

2 Foods that contain additives or E numbers are artificial products which are used to improve the colour or taste of food or increase the shelf life of the food. Some of these additives have been found to be harmful to health so should be avoided to help ensure a person is eating a healthy diet.

3 Organic foods are often a more healthy option compared to foods that have not been grown organically as they will often contain more vitamins and minerals. This is because organic foods are not treated with pesticides or fertilizers which research suggests increases their stores of vitamins. Where possible, organic foods should be consumed as part of a healthy diet.

It's important to remember that what you choose to eat will actually be used to become a part of your body or affect the way your body functions.

ACTIVITY

Make a list of foods that you have eaten or are aware of that are processed.

In your list state the food in its processed form and then next to it what it would be in its natural form.

CHECK MY LEARNING

Identify the recommended percentage intake of the following macronutrients for a healthy diet:
- carbohydrates
- fat
- protein.

Explain why it is important to eat at least three meals a day.

Methods to enhance sport and activity through nutritional change (1)

Taking part in sports and activities places different demands on the body and nutrition can have a significant impact on enhancing performance.

Any person taking part in sport and activity will need to factor into their diet their body's requirements of:
- replacing the energy lost during training
- repairing any damage done to the body's structures during training
- ensuring sufficient quantities of vitamins and minerals are consumed to ensure correct functioning of all the body's systems
- replacing and maintaining their fluid levels.

The type of sport or activity will determine how nutrition needs to be tailored to meet and enhance performance for that person.

Carbohydrate loading

Our body stores carbohydrate in our muscles and liver in the form of glycogen. However, this store is relatively small and there is only enough to supply energy for around 1.5–2 hours of exercise at moderate to high intensity. Any person who takes part in sports or activities that last longer than this would not normally have sufficient carbohydrate stores to allow them to continue exercising at the same intensity, and they would have to slow down to a walk or stop the activity.

A nutritional strategy called 'carbohydrate loading' helps to increase the amount of carbohydrate a person can store and is used by people taking part in events such as marathon running, which last over two hours. The strategy involves both training and nutritional changes over a four-day period immediately before the sport or activity event, as shown in Figure 2.17, with a complete rest on the last day before the event. On each of these days they consume higher than normal quantities of carbohydrates, around 10 to 12 g per kg of bodyweight.

◻ Loading up on carbohydrates the night before a marathon helps runners sustain their energy throughout the event and helps them to avoid 'hitting the wall'.

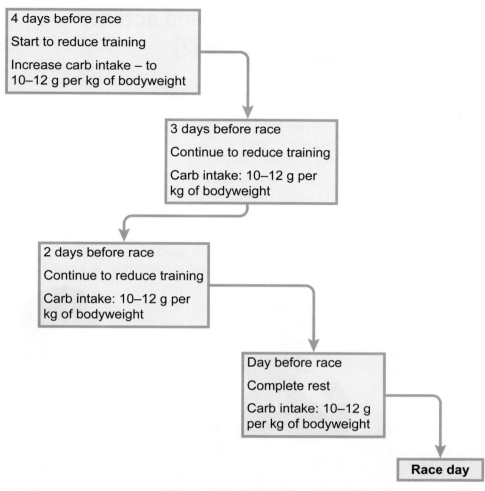

■ Figure 2.17: This process of reducing exercise levels and increasing carbohydrate
   intake increases the body's stores of carbohydrate ready to be used to supply energy
   for a specific sport or activity

ACTIVITY

Carry out research to find out the current male and female world record
time for completing a marathon. Also research the average time for non-elite
runners to complete this distance. Explain if you think world class athletes would
need to carbohydrate load prior to taking part in a marathon, giving reasons for
your answer.

CHECK MY LEARNING

1 Explain what is meant by carbohydrate loading.
2 Describe three events where the performance of participants would be
   positively affected from carbohydrate loading prior to taking part in the event,
   giving reasons for your choices.

Methods to enhance sport and activity through nutritional change (2)

GETTING STARTED

Think about the sorts of foods and drinks that you eat before, during and after an event. Are there any particular foods or drinks that you prefer? Make a list of each, giving reasons why you consume those foods and fluids. Are there any foods and fluids which have made you feel unwell or which have affected your performance and you now avoid? Make a list of these too, suggesting reasons why you think they had a negative effect on you.

Timing of food intake and types of food

For all sports and activities there are three main phases. Each phase needs to be considered in relation to what sorts of foods and fluids should be consumed in order to maximise energy for training as well as competition.

These three phases are:
- pre-event – this is the night before and the first few hours the next day before the event or training starts
- during the event – while the person is exercising, for example during a football match or when they are on a break during a tennis match
- post-event – the first two hours immediately after the competition or training.

■ Figure 2.18: The types of food and drink taken during the three phases of an event

Pre-event

One of the main aims in maximising nutrition before the event or training is to ensure the body's stores of carbohydrate are well stocked. If a person is taking part in an event that lasts over two hours, the pre-event would also include the carbohydrate-loading process. For events lasting two hours or less, the pre-event time frame is just taking into account the night before and the first few hours prior to the event itself.

To do this, complex carbohydrates should be consumed to help to fully stock up the body's stores of carbohydrates. Foods such as pasta, potatoes or rice are complex carbohydrates and would be suitable foods to eat the night before.

Just before the event is about to start, simple carbohydrates should be consumed to help to maximise glucose availability, so it can be used as an energy source as soon as the person starts their event or training. Foods such as glucose tablets, jelly beans or other types of sweets would be suitable foods to eat before the activity is about to start. It is best to avoid foods that contain high levels of fat and protein as they take a long time to digest and can cause stomach cramps.

During the event

When taking part in an event that lasts for 90 minutes or longer, it is important to try to save the carbohydrate stores in the body, so consuming foods or fluids that contain carbohydrates during the event or training will be of benefit to the individual as they will provide energy. The body will use carbohydrates consumed during exercise as a fuel and this will help to conserve the body's carbohydrate stores. Some athletes eat sweets like jelly beans to provide glucose; sports drinks that contain carbohydrates are also a popular choice as they are easy to digest and also provide fluids to help to maintain hydration (required to maximise sporting performance).

Post-event

After training or competition, it is important that the right foods and fluids are consumed to maximise recovery. The sooner the person recovers the sooner they can take part in more training to help to improve their performance.

Foods and drinks containing protein will help to repair the micro tears that occur in muscle tissue after having taken part in many different sports and activities, especially ones that require muscular strength. Milk or milk-based drinks such as milkshakes are a good source of protein and are a popular post-sport or activity recovery drink. As well as being easy to carry, they are easily digested and refreshing to consume.

In addition, carbohydrate stores should be replaced after training or competition. During the first two hours post-event, your body is able to convert carbohydrates into glycogen (the body's store of carbohydrate) at a very fast rate. Milkshakes contain carbohydrates, and carbohydrate bars and energy gels can also be consumed to provide the body with sources of carbohydrates to refuel its carbohydrate stores.

Bowel emptying

While it is important to ensure we are eating the right foods and drinking the right fluids to maximise nutrition, it is also important to consider consuming foods that are high in fibre. This helps the digestion process and the excretion of waste products in a timely and comfortable manner. If a person is suffering from bowel emptying concerns such as constipation it will make them feel uncomfortable when taking part in exercise and can negatively affect performance. It is therefore important to ensure sufficient foods are consumed that contain fibre to help with the process of bowel emptying.

Timing of food intake is also important. Some foods can take a while to digest, especially foods with a high fat and protein content. When foods are being digested, blood is directed to the digestive system to help with the digestive processes. However, when a person exercises, blood is needed by the working muscles to supply oxygen and nutrients. This means blood is directed away from the digestive system and can produce the feelings of nausea or stitches that you feel if you have eaten too soon prior to taking part in sport or activity.

ACTIVITY

Identify foods that would be beneficial for a gymnast to eat at the following times:
- before their training
- during a three-hour training session
- after their training session.

Give reasons for your choices.

CHECK MY LEARNING

For the following sports performers, explain a nutritional change that may be beneficial to their performance:
- an ironman triathlete one week before the event
- a weightlifter after completing a heavy training session
- a cross-country runner who always feels the need to go to the toilet during their race.

Legal supplements

GETTING STARTED

In a small group discuss what you know about the term 'supplements'. Describe places where you have seen supplements advertised and what sorts of benefits a person may hope to experience if they take these supplements.

There is a huge market in supplements, many of which contain advertising stating that they will help to improve sport and activity performance. The products covered in this section are all given the term 'legal supplements' which means sports people can take these supplements if they are competing. Research indicates that many legal supplements can enhance performance but the supplement has to be specific to certain types of sport or activity in order to be beneficial to performance. There are also negative effects from taking some supplements, such as caffeine which provides energy peaks followed by troughs where the person will feel very tired and lethargic.

Vitamins B and D

LINK IT UP

See page 117 Micronutrients – vitamins and minerals for more on vitamin B (pages 116–117).

If a person is consuming a varied diet which contains foods that are rich in vitamins B and D, then supplementation is probably unnecessary. However, as vitamin B is a water-soluble vitamin which means it cannot be stored in the body, it may be beneficial for athletes who take part in regular sport and activity to take vitamin B supplements. This vitamin helps to convert food into energy, so it is very important in helping to ensure the working muscles are able to receive sufficient energy to allow the person to exercise for their preferred periods of time.

Vitamin D helps to maintain bone and muscle health which are vital for sport and activity performance. It can be found in a variety of foods and it can be made by the body if the body receives sunlight. It may be beneficial for people who take part in sport and activity to take a vitamin D supplement in the winter months when their skin is exposed to very little sunshine and they may not be eating sufficient sources of the food in their diet.

Some types of diets such as vegetarianism or veganism may mean it is difficult to consume sufficient quantities of vitamins B and D, especially vitamin D which is found mainly in foods that come from animal sources.

Protein supplements

People who take part in sports and activities that require high levels of strength will usually need a high muscle mass to perform well in their selected sport or activity. As you know, protein is needed in the diet to help with muscle growth and repair. Protein supplements are designed for people who want to lay down more muscle and need to consume more protein than average. As it may be difficult for some people to consume all their protein requirements from their daily food, a range of protein supplements have been devised that deliver high concentrations of protein. Protein supplements are usually made from powdered milk, eggs and/or, as a vegan option, soya.

Protein supplements are commonly found in the form of protein shakes that contain high levels of amino acids and are quick to drink and convenient to use. Protein bars are also available which again are quick to eat. Both protein shakes and bars deliver high concentrations of protein and low levels of carbohydrates, with very little or no fat.

However, there are some concerns with protein supplements as the human body has evolved to gain its protein from natural sources such as meat and eggs rather than processed sources such as powders and bars. The process of drying the proteins into powder affects the structure of the amino acids and may damage them, which may have an impact on how well the body can use them. Another disadvantage is that protein supplements will often contain additives such as sweeteners, sugars and/or colourings, and are often quite expensive too.

Pre-workout supplements

A wide range of pre-workout supplements are available, which are usually designed to provide a burst of energy. Examples of pre-workout supplements are energy gels and glucose tablets. An energy gel is a mixture between a sports drink and an energy bar, rather like a runny jelly. Glucose tablets are similar but in a harder format like a sweet. Both gels and tablets contain high levels of carbohydrate and very little protein and fat. Many athletes choose to consume these before or during exercise as they deliver higher levels of carbohydrate than sports drinks, are easy and quick to consume and cause little or no stomach discomfort.

Glucose-based isotonic drinks

Glucose-based **isotonic** drinks are the most popular type of sports drink as they help the body to rehydrate and also provide energy in the form of simple carbohydrates. An isotonic sports drink will have between 4 g and 8 g of sugar per 100 ml fluid. As an isotonic drink has a similar concentration of dissolved solids as our blood, the fluid is absorbed very quickly into the body so that we rehydrate very quickly.

However, these drinks are high in calories so if a person has not used up the calories when taking part in their sport or activity it can lead to weight gain. The sugar in the drinks could also contribute to tooth decay.

Caffeine drinks

Caffeine is found in drinks such as coffee and tea as well as cola drinks. Caffeine is also added to sports and energy drinks. The effect of caffeine on the body is to increase energy levels and alertness and to improve reaction times.

Research also indicates that caffeine can reduce a person's perception of effort when they are taking part in sport or activity, which may help them to exercise at a higher intensity and have a positive impact on their performance.

Caffeine also increases the use of fats as an energy source. People who take part in long distance aerobic endurance events will therefore benefit from taking a caffeine sports drink because using body fat as an energy source has the effect of sparing the body's carbohydrate stores.

However, there are disadvantages of using caffeine as it can have some negative side effects such as insomnia, anxiety, diarrhoea and high blood pressure. In addition, when the effects of caffeine wear off it can produce energy troughs, leaving the person feeling very tired and lethargic.

Up until 2004 caffeine was only permitted in certain sports at specific levels which equated to around six to eight cups of coffee. Currently the World Anti-Doping Agency (WADA) is monitoring the use of caffeine and may decide to reinstate permitted levels.

KEY TERM

Isotonic is a solution that has the same osmotic pressure as the body's fluids. This essentially means it has a similar concentration of dissolved solids as our blood.

CHECK MY LEARNING

For the following sports performers, explain what sorts of supplements they may benefit from taking, giving reasons for each choice:
- shot put thrower
- long-distance open water swimmer
- cricket player.

Learning aim B: assessment practice

How you will be assessed

All of this component is assessed through a written assessment which is set and marked by Pearson.

The written external assessment will contain short and extended questions which cover each learning aim in the component.

CHECKPOINT

Strengthen

- Know what a healthy diet consists of.
- Know how macronutrients affect the body's ability to function during sport and activity.
- Know how micronutrients affect the body's ability to function during sport and activity.
- Understand how hydration affects participation in sport and activity.
- Be able to review a diet and suggest improvements for participation in selected sports or activities.

Challenge

- Justify why different macronutrients are beneficial to participation in different types of sports and activities.
- Justify why different micronutrients are beneficial to participation in different types of sports and activities.
- Assess the benefits of hydration for participation in sport and activity.
- Provide advantages and disadvantages of dietary changes, including supplements, to increase sport or activity performance.

ASSESSMENT ACTIVITY | LEARNING AIM | B

1 a) Identify a food source that is high in protein. (1 mark)

b) State a function of fat. (1 mark)

c) Identify a vitamin. (1 mark)

d) Explain the difference between a simple and complex carbohydrate. (4 marks)

e) State what is meant by a calorie. (1 mark)

2 Janine takes part in weightlifting competitions.

a) Explain why protein is an important part of Janine's diet. (3 marks)

b) Describe what is meant by dehydration. (2 marks)

c) Identify the recommended daily intake (RDI) of fluid in normal conditions. (1 mark)

d) Explain the benefits of hydration for sport and activity. (3 marks)

e) Identify two foods that can be eaten to help to support the bowel emptying process. (2 marks)

TIPS

While you are studying this component, always try and read nutritional labels on all the foods that you eat. This should give you a good idea of the percentage of macronutrients in each type of food, as well as any micronutrients they contain.

TAKE IT FURTHER

Justify nutritional and hydration guidance that you would provide for a marathon runner, including any legal supplements that may be beneficial to performance during the following stages:

- one week before the event
- the breakfast before the event
- during the event
- after the event.

The impact of motivation on participation in sport and activity

Psychology is the study of the mind and how it affects behaviours. Sport psychology is therefore the study of how the mind affects sporting behaviours and actions. You will have seen elite sports performers behaving in negative ways – such as tennis players breaking their racket in response to an umpire's decision or a footballer fighting with an opponent on the pitch as they believed that they had been fouled. These are examples of how the mind can affect sporting actions and result in negative consequences.

However, there are many positive outcomes studied in sport psychology too, which explore why people do certain things to help them to achieve great success. One of the main reasons for this is related to motivation.

Motivation

Motivation is the drive for a person to be successful to achieve a specific goal. A person who is highly motivated will put in a lot of effort and give up things that are important to them in order to keep working towards achieving their goal.

These can be related to internal mechanisms and external stimuli that arouse and direct behaviour.

There are two main types of motivation:
- intrinsic motivation
- extrinsic motivation.

Intrinsic motivation

Intrinsic motivation is related to internal mechanisms that encourage a person to behave in a certain way. An intrinsic mechanism is essentially the way it makes a person feel. So for intrinsic motivation, a person would take part in a particular sport or activity because they enjoy taking part and get enough pleasure from it to want to make them keep participating – essentially, they enjoy doing it and it makes them happy.

An example of a person who is intrinsically motivated is someone who goes cross-country running three times a week because they enjoy the feeling of being out in the country and exercising their body. They have no external influences and feel under no pressure from anyone else to go jogging; they simply enjoy running and being out in the fresh air.

Extrinsic motivation

This is where some form of reward is given for taking part or doing well in a sport or activity, such as receiving a medal for attending a sports camp or winning a trophy or prize money; the thought of gaining some form of reward is the reason the person takes part in the sport or activity. The rewards can be called **tangible** or **intangible**.

A tangible reward is a financial reward such as winning money, or getting something for free that would normally cost money such as a trophy, a gym membership or electronic goods. An intangible reward is something that does not cost anything but provides some form of recognition, for example praise, having your name in a local newspaper for an achievement, being made captain of the school netball team, etc.

An example of a person who is extrinsically motivated is someone who goes out running three times a week so that they are ready to take part in 5 km running races and can receive the rewards associated with winning.

This person gains most satisfaction from beating the other runners in the race and likes the idea that their friends and family see them as a good runner, which makes them feel popular and a better person.

◨ Winning a tangible reward like a trophy can be a strong motivational factor.

◨ Table 2.32: Motivating factors for running three times a week

Intrinsic	Extrinsic
Enjoys being outside in the fresh air	Likes to be seen as a good runner
Likes the feeling of exercise	Wants to beat other competitors in a race
Makes them feel happy	Wants to be awarded a medal

ACTIVITY

Explain whether the following participants are intrinsically or extrinsically motivated.
- Jed takes part in badminton competitions as he likes the feeling of winning and wants to add more trophies to his trophy cabinet.
- Zeina takes part in weightlifting because she likes the way it makes her body look.
- Pawan takes part in 100-metre sprinting as he wants to be the best sprinter for his age group in the country.
- Anna takes part in mountain biking as she likes to be out in the countryside.
- Marta takes part in swimming as she likes to have the badges for the distances she has covered sewn on her swimsuit.

CHECK MY LEARNING

1 Explain what motivates you to take part in your selected sports and/or activities.

2 Identify if your motivation is intrinsic or extrinsic for each sport or activity, giving reasons for your response.

The impact of motivation on participation in sport and activity – benefits

Increasing motivation levels can have a significant positive impact on participation in sport and activity in many ways. It is therefore an important part of sport psychology to try and ensure participants are sufficiently motivated: we know participation is hugely beneficial to health and well-being.

◧ High motivation levels can help people to push themselves harder in sport and activities.

Intensity of effort during participation is higher

If a person is motivated to take part in a sport or activity they will feel more able to push themselves harder and therefore be able to exercise at a higher intensity. For example, when running it may feel like an easier option to slow down when faced with having to run up a hill. However, if a person is sufficiently motivated they will feel that they want to try as hard as they can and run as fast as they are able to up that hill. This will cause some discomfort as working at a high intensity stresses the body. But a highly motivated person will usually be able to put up with this discomfort because their mind is driving them on to succeed; this means that they are more able to achieve whatever is motivating them to take part in the sport or activity.

Continuing to take part on a regular basis

We should take part in sport and activity on a regular basis each week for fitness and health gains. Many people have started an exercise programme and felt very motivated at the beginning, but after a few weeks motivation levels often drop and the same drive to take part in the exercise programme can fade. Also, when a person is tired after a day at work or school, it can be hard to then take part in sport or activity – sitting down and relaxing may be the preferred option. However, if motivation levels are sufficiently high and maintained, it will help participants to overcome any thoughts of not taking part in the sport or activity and ensure that they participate on a regular basis.

Overcoming adversity

Adversity is something that is upsetting or unpleasant. Adverse situations related to participation in fitness could be:

- being injured and unable to participate for an extended period of time
- not achieving a specific fitness goal in the planned time frame
- something beyond participation in fitness but which has an effect on that person.

Examples of things which may adversely influence a person's desire to participate in sport and activity are getting a bad school report, falling out with a friend, or something significant such as a bereavement.

However, if someone has high levels of motivation, it can help them to overcome these adverse situations and continue to participate in fitness training. This can either be immediately or when they are physically able to.

Higher enjoyment levels

When a person is highly motivated they will enjoy participation in fitness to a greater degree than if they weren't highly motivated. This is because they will not have those negative feelings that many people have prior to taking part in fitness training. They will usually be looking forward to their fitness training because it is something that they know they will enjoy. Once they have taken part in the fitness training, these feelings of enjoyment will continue as the person will be pleased that they have completed the set training and know the benefits it will bring them.

Increased intrinsic and extrinsic rewards

Taking part in regular fitness training will bring with it increased intrinsic rewards. This is because the person will continue to enjoy the feeling of taking part in the training and benefit after participating as they know they have done something that they have enjoyed.

For those people who are motivated by extrinsic rewards, they will be more likely to gain these rewards from performing well in their selected sport or activity. This is especially the case if they have taken part in enough fitness training for their body to adapt to improve performance in the selected sport or activity. The more prizes or rewards the person achieves, the more motivated they are likely to be to want to go on and win more extrinsic rewards.

> **CHECK MY LEARNING** ■ ■ ■
>
> Geraint is starting a cycling club to encourage young people to take part in competitive cycling.
>
> Explain why it is important for Geraint to increase the motivation of the young people in his cycling club. Include in your answer how it will be beneficial to the club and how it will be beneficial to the participants.

The impact of self-confidence on participation in sport and activity

GETTING STARTED

When you hear the term self-confidence, which sports people do you think of? With a partner, make a list of all the sports people you have seen or know that you think have high levels of self-confidence. Explain why you think this and if you feel this has an effect on their sporting performance.

Self-confidence

Self-confidence is the belief that a desired behaviour can be performed. The more self-confident a person is, the greater their belief that they are able to do something. However, the less self-confident a person is, the lower their belief that they are able to do something.

Self-confidence can have a significant impact on a person's ability to participate and succeed in everyday situations as well as in high-level competition.

In sport and activity-related situations, high levels of self-confidence are regarded as positive and something to strive for.

Benefits of self-confidence

There are many benefits of high levels of self-confidence, as shown in Figure 2.19.

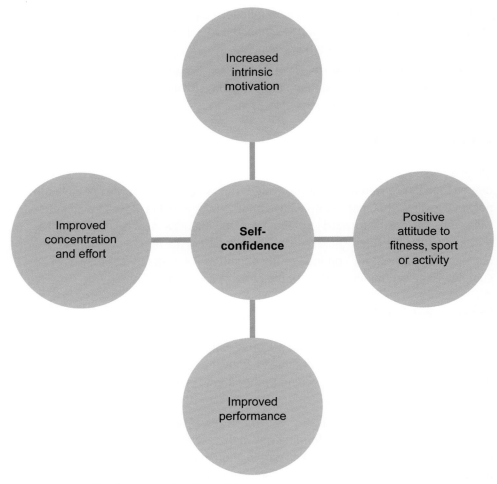

◘ **Figure 2.19: The benefits of self-confidence**

Increased intrinsic motivation

Having high levels of self-confidence can help to increase intrinsic motivation. As you have seen in the section on motivation, high levels of motivation can help to increase participation levels, which is beneficial for health and well-being as well as for improving the chances of sporting success.

Positive attitude to fitness, sport or activity

An attitude is something that influences the action a person chooses to take and their response to challenges and rewards. A positive attitude to fitness, sport or activity will increase the belief of a participant that they can reach their goal, whatever it may be. Whether it is to be able to run 5 km in less than 30 minutes or become a professional basketball player, having a positive attitude is important to help that person take part in all the training and preparation required to help them to achieve their goal.

Improved performance

Having high levels of self-confidence can help to improve a person's performance levels. This is because a person with high levels of self-confidence believes that they are capable of performing at a certain level; they will not be put off and made to feel inferior by other participants. High levels of self-confidence are important in team games such as rugby or football; for example, when a person is going in for a tackle they will fully commit to it and are therefore more likely to be successful compared to another player who thinks the person they are about to tackle is much better than them (and therefore they will not be good enough to tackle them correctly).

Improved concentration and effort

High levels of self-confidence help a person to just focus on the sport or activity in hand rather than on any doubts or concerns about their own ability and performance. Having concerns about your own performance requires mental effort and takes the focus away from the actual sport or activity being performed. This means you are not able to fully concentrate on participating. However, not being concerned about one's own abilities helps to keep the focus on what is going on around you. It will also help to increase the amount of effort put into participating which will have the overall effect of improving performance.

CHECK MY LEARNING

Explain four benefits of having self-confidence for a person who takes part in sport or activity.

Methods to increase self-confidence

We know that self-confidence is beneficial for sport and activity performance. There are methods a sport or activity leader can use to help to improve the self-confidence of participants so that they can get the most out of their sport or activity session.

Positive reinforcement

Leaders of sport and activity can provide extrinsic motivation through positive reinforcement. This involves the addition of a reinforcing stimulus following a behaviour that makes it more likely that the behaviour will occur again. When a favourable outcome occurs after an action, that particular response or behaviour will be strengthened. This reinforcing stimulus could be verbal, such as saying 'Well done', or non-verbal, such as a thumbs up. It can also be in the form of a reward.

Rewards

When participants work hard they often like to receive some form of reward to recognise the effort and commitment that they have put in. Children in particular respond well to having some form of recognition in the form of a reward. Many sports leaders will provide badges or certificates to participants to acknowledge hard work or the achievement of a certain skill or ability level.

ACTIVITY

Write down the different sports that you took part in when you were younger.

What forms of rewards were given out to participants during these sports?

How did receiving these rewards make you feel?

Creating a positive environment

☐ A sports leader celebrating their team's achievements with them can help create a positive environment.

It is important that a sports or activity leader creates a positive environment so that participants feel comfortable when they are exercising. The sports leader should be able to assess how the participants are responding to how they are leading the session. They should then modify their behaviour to suit them; for example, in a boot camp, some participants may respond well to being shouted at to encourage them to work harder, whereas other people may find this off-putting and not respond well. A positive environment can also be created by praising people's efforts and noticing when a person has been able to do something that they haven't been able to do before. This helps the participant to feel they belong in the sport or activity environment and they are therefore more likely to try their hardest in the sessions.

Working with a training partner of similar ability

Having a training partner or buddy can be very motivating. If someone is feeling tired and not in the mood to go to a sport or activity session, having a friend who is keen to go will often make that person feel that they should go too – otherwise they are letting their friend down. Having a partner will also add a sociable element to the training session.

It is important that a training partner is of similar ability, especially if you are looking to train with that person. For example, if you go running with someone of a higher ability it could be demotivating if you are not able to keep up with them, or you may feel like giving up if you can see they are much better than you.

Goal setting

A good method of developing motivation is to use goal setting to set realistic goals for the fitness session.

This form of motivational technique involves the sport or activity leader setting **goals** for an individual or group of participants. These goals should be both short-term and long-term and are put in place to help a person to progress. A short-term goal is something that a person can achieve in just a few weeks or even at the end of one activity session. A long-term goal is set over a longer period of time such as a block of six weeks, or a school term, or even longer.

An example of a short-term goal would be for a person to be able to run 5 km in less than 35 minutes. The long-term goal could then be to run a marathon in 10 months' time.

The goals a sports or activity leader sets with participants should be SMART. This means they should be:

- **S**pecific –the goal must be related to something that a participant wants to achieve.
- **M**easurable – the goal has to be able to be monitored so that a participant can see how well they are progressing towards their goal.
- **A**chievable – the goal has to be something that the participant is capable of doing.
- **R**ealistic – any barriers that the participant may face should be considered when setting a goal to ensure there is nothing that could prevent them from achieving the set goal.
- **T**ime-related – there should be a timescale set that the participant is trying to achieve the set goal in.

For example:

I am 15 years old and can run 5 km in 40 minutes. In 5 weeks (**time-related**) *I want to be able to run 5 km* (**achievable** as they are running 5 km in 40 minutes already and **measurable** as a time frame is given) *in 25 minutes* (**specific** and **realistic** given the 5-week time frame).

A good way to help to set goals to motivate a person is to answer three questions.
- What is my set goal?
- What am I able to do now related to my set goal?
- What do I need to do to achieve my set goal?

Self-talk

This is where a person literally talks to themselves, either out loud or in their head. Self-talk involves stating key messages called affirmations which reassure a person they have what is needed to be successful and complete a specific task. This helps to psychologically motivate the person to achieve their desired goal. Examples of self-talk to motivate a person could include statements such as 'Come on, you can do this' or 'I know I can do this, only 10 more seconds to go', etc.

Self-talk is often used when a person is starting to feel very uncomfortable when they are exercising at a high intensity or for a long period of time and it would be much easier to simply stop or slow down during the fitness session. However, self-talk can help to motivate a person to continue and complete the whole session.

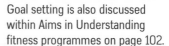

LINK IT UP

Goal setting is also discussed within Aims in Understanding fitness programmes on page 102.

KEY TERM

A **goal** is something an individual wants to achieve.

ACTIVITY

For a sport or activity that you take part in, identify your set goal, describe where you are now related to your goal, and then explain what you need to do to achieve this set goal.

CHECK MY LEARNING

If you were a sports leader for a sport or activity session, explain how you would help to increase self-confidence for the following groups of participants:
- children aged 5 to 6 years learning how to play football
- older adults aged 65+ taking part in an exercise session
- an under-14 basketball team hoping to make it to the regional finals.

The impact of anxiety on participation in sport and activity (1)

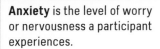

Anxiety is regarded as an undesirable emotion and can have a negative effect on participation in sport and activity. It is therefore important to understand the reasons why a participant may become anxious and the ways in which anxiety can be reduced to help to promote increased participation in sport and activity.

Types of anxiety

There are two main types of anxiety:
- state anxiety – this refers to a particular situation; state anxiety may arise when there is a high-pressure situation and the participant must perform
- trait anxiety – this is where the participant is tense and apprehensive as a characteristic of their personality and therefore anxiety is a consistent feeling for them.

State anxiety

This is related to the situation a person is in. An example of this would be where a person who is not usually anxious may start to have feelings of anxiety when they are about to take part in an important competition. This type of anxiety is temporary and may only occur in certain situations.

Trait anxiety

Some people are naturally more anxious than other people in similar situations. People with high levels of trait anxiety are more likely to feel anxious in situations where other people do not feel any anxiety at all, so this type of anxiety is related to an individual's personality to some degree rather than a temporary feeling.

Effects of anxiety on participation in sport and activity

Anxiety can affect a person in two different ways: one is how the body reacts and the other is how the mind reacts. These are called somatic and cognitive anxiety.

Somatic anxiety

Somatic anxiety refers to the physical effects that are brought on by state and/or trait anxiety. The feelings of somatic anxiety a person can experience include:
- butterflies in the stomach, which can make a person feel nauseous and not able to eat or drink anything before or during participation
- muscle tension, which makes a person feel stiff and tense and which will have an effect on performance as having tense muscles will affect the person's technique when they are trying to perform a specific skill in a sport or activity
- increased heart rate
- increased sweat rate.

Cognitive anxiety

This type of anxiety refers to the psychological effects that are brought on by state and/or trait anxiety.

The psychological effects a person can experience include:
- feeling worried, which distracts the person and means they lose their focus on what they are supposed to be doing
- poor concentration levels, which means they are not as fully committed to the sport or activity as they are thinking of other things
- lack of sleep due to overthinking, which may mean the person is tired which will have a negative effect on performance.

ACTIVITY

There are a number of different tests, such as the State-Trait Anxiety Inventory (STAI), available on the internet to find out about your own anxiety levels and if you are more prone to have state or trait anxiety.

Carry out one of these tests and write a paragraph to explain the results of the test. State if you agree with what the test suggested in relation to you and if you have higher levels of state or trait anxiety.

CHECK MY LEARNING

1 Explain the difference between state and trait anxiety.
2 State the type of anxiety that produces physical effects on the body.
3 Describe four physical effects of anxiety on the body.
4 Identify the type of anxiety that produces psychological effects on the body.
5 Explain three psychological effects of anxiety.

The impact of anxiety on participation in sport and activity (2)

Controlling anxiety plays an important role in encouraging people to take part in sport and activity. Many people who have not taken part in sport or activity for a while may feel very anxious about taking the first steps in joining a gym or an exercise class. Some people may feel anxious that they are not going to be good enough to join a sports club such as a hockey team, so decide not to join.

Methods of controlling anxiety

There are a number of ways a sport or activity leader can help to reduce and control anxiety as it is important that people have the opportunity to participate. They need to overcome their nervousness and support will help them to do this.

Fitness induction

Virtually all gyms and health clubs require a participant to attend an induction which is designed to familiarise new members with the facilities and equipment. This helps a person to overcome any anxiety they have about not knowing where to go or how to use the equipment. It is also a key requirement for health and safety, because if a person does not know how to use equipment properly it can result in injury.

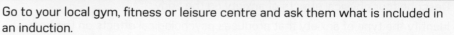

ACTIVITY

Go to your local gym, fitness or leisure centre and ask them what is included in an induction.

If you have already been through an induction, think back to what was included and how you felt about going to the centre before and after the induction.

Describe the process and explain how you think this would help to reduce anxiety for new members of the centre.

Use of music

Music can have a significant effect on a person's emotions. Some music can be highly motivating and encourage a person to exercise at a higher intensity, whereas other types of music can have a calming effect. Many people enjoy listening to their own choice of music when exercising and use personal music devices with music tracks that have been downloaded that can be used for different parts of an exercise session. Some fitness sessions are carried out to music, such as circuits or Zumba. In these situations, the exercise instructor is responsible for selecting the music. It is important that they choose music that will appeal to the participants, to help to motivate them to participate as well as helping to lower their anxiety levels.

◻ Listening to music when exercising can be motivational and also lower anxiety levels.

List songs that you like to listen to that help to:
- motivate you
- calm you down and reduce anxiety levels.

Examine if there are any trends in the types of music that you listen to that motivate you and any trends in music that has a calming effect.

Explain why you think specific types of music help to motivate you and why other types have a calming effect.

Classes and activities based on ability levels

If you look at most fitness centres' timetables for exercise classes, outdoor activities and sports training, they will have some way of identifying which levels of fitness each exercise class is suitable for, such as beginner, intermediate and advanced. Ensuring classes are targeted at a specific ability level will help participants to sign up to attend the class as they will feel comfortable if they know the class is aimed at the right level for them. This means they will feel confident that the types of activities will be appropriate for them and that they will have the fitness levels required to participate. This will also help them to avoid feelings of inferiority which may happen if they were in a class with people who were much fitter and able to do much more than them. In the same way, sports clubs will have training available for different abilities to help to ensure the training is appropriate for the level of ability of the participants.

Pre-match team talk

Before taking part in any kind of match or competition, many people may feel anxious and start to worry about whether they are good enough, or that the opposing person or team will be better than them. They may worry that they could let their team down if they don't play well or that their friends and family who are watching will think they are not very good at their sport.

These worries and concerns are quite natural, which is why a pre-match team talk is often carried out by the coach, manager or captain to try and reduce anxiety levels. The team talk will usually focus on the positives such as 'You've all done really well in training and are ready for this match' which helps the participants to feel that they are capable of doing well as their coach believes in them. If the participants respect the person giving the pre-match team talk, they will think that person knows more than them and they are being silly to worry and be anxious. This will result in them having higher levels of self-confidence and help them to perform as well as possible in the match.

For each situation, suggest methods that could be used to reduce anxiety and give reasons for your answer:
- a young mother who wants to go to the gym but hasn't exercised or been to a gym for five years
- an under-14 handball team about to take part in a play-off for the regional final
- a circuit instructor hoping to work the class as hard as possible in the last circuit.

Learning aim C: assessment practice

How you will be assessed

All of this component is assessed through a written assessment which is set and marked by Pearson.

The written external assessment will contain short and extended questions which cover each learning aim in the component.

CHECKPOINT

Strengthen

- Understand internal and external types of motivation.
- Know the benefits of increased motivation on fitness participation levels.
- Understand the benefits of self-confidence.
- Be able to discuss methods to increase self-confidence.
- Understand the different types of anxiety.
- Know how anxiety affects participation in sport and activity.
- Understand methods that can be used to control anxiety.

Challenge

- Assess how motivation affects participation in sport and activity.
- Analyse the impact of self-confidence on participation in sport and activity.
- Justify methods that can be used to control anxiety.

ASSESSMENT ACTIVITY | **LEARNING AIM** | **C**

Sheena plays tennis with her friends as she enjoys being outside and playing sport. Her doubles partner, Sue, likes taking part in competitions as she enjoys winning trophies and getting the recognition of doing well in tennis.

1 a) Identify the type of motivation that encourages Sheena to play tennis. (1 mark)

   b) Identify the type of motivation that encourages Sue to play tennis. (1 mark)

2 Describe why motivation is beneficial for participation in tennis.

   Sheena has high levels of self-confidence.

3 Explain why this is beneficial for her tennis-playing performance. (2 marks)

   Sue, however, has low levels of self-confidence.

4 Describe two ways to help to improve Sue's self-confidence. (4 marks)

   Sue and Sheena are due to take part in a regional tennis tournament.

   Sue is feeling anxious about taking part in the tournament.

5 Explain how high levels of anxiety can have a negative effect on performance. (3 marks)

6 Describe one way to decrease Sue's anxiety before the tennis tournament. (2 marks)

TIPS

Make sure you know all the different methods to increase self-confidence and also to control anxiety, as some methods are going to be more appropriate for a participant for their selected sport or activity.

TAKE IT FURTHER

Explore how high-level sports teams and health and fitness providers use the range of methods included in the specification to increase self-confidence and decrease anxiety for different types of participants.

COMPONENT

03 Applying the Principles of Sport and Activity

Introduction

This component consolidates your learning from Components 1 and 2, and applies it to the context of sport and activity leadership.

You will learn about the attributes of a sports leader and how each of them help the leader to plan and deliver a successful sport or activity session. You will also explore the short-term and long-term physical and psychological benefits for participants who take part in regular sport and activity.

You will look at different types of participants, together with the types of sport or activity sessions that will help to engage them and encourage regular participation.

The planning of a sport or activity session will be covered, including the different components of a session and how to plan for different types of sessions.

Lastly, you will look at the factors to consider when delivering and then reviewing a sport or activity session.

LEARNING AIMS

In this component you will:

A	Understand the fundamentals of sport and activity leadership
B	Plan sessions for target groups
C	Deliver and review sessions for target groups.

Attributes of a leader: skills (1)

A successful leader requires many attributes to help to ensure the participants they are leading fully understand and engage in the sport or activity, so that they can get the most out of the session and also keep attending the sport or activity sessions.

Communication

Communication can be **verbal** or **non-verbal.**

Verbal communication

How a sports leader speaks to participants is very important and there are a number of areas a sports leader should consider.

Tone of voice – this is the pitch, level and sound of your voice, which can be used to express how you are feeling. For example, if a person is feeling happy the tone is usually higher and softer, but when someone is feeling angry the tone is deeper and louder. If a sports leader is trying to encourage participants, the tone of their voice should reflect this. A sports leader's tone should also vary to help to add emphasis to key words or messages.

Volume – as a sports leader, you need to make sure each person can hear you, so you should speak clearly and sufficiently loud to be heard. In a sporting environment, a sports leader may need to raise their voice to be heard over the background noise of people playing sport. To help to ensure participants can hear, a sports leader should face the people that they are speaking to, so that their voice travels towards them. This also allows the sports leader to check that participants are listening to them. When giving feedback, speaking more softly can be beneficial so that the participant does not feel like they are being shouted at and listens carefully to what is being said.

Use of appropriate vocabulary for the audience – try not to say too much and try to avoid technical terms. You need to make sure all participants understand what you are saying and they may not all be familiar with sport-specific technical terms. A sports leader should gradually introduce technical terms at appropriate points related to the participants, developing expertise and experience.

Distance – when using verbal communication with participants, it is important to remember that there is an acceptable distance to stand from another person so as not to invade their 'personal space'. Therefore, a sports leader needs to stand close enough to be heard but not too close, as this may make a person feel uncomfortable.

Non-verbal communication

Many sports leaders will use non-verbal communication with participants. Non-verbal communication involves a variety of different methods which all include using body language.

Appropriate body language – the body language a person uses can help to show people what they are thinking and how motivated they are when performing certain activities. For example, if a person is standing up straight and looking focused on a person or an activity, it shows that they are interested and concentrating on that person so they have their full attention. However, if a person is standing with their hands in their pockets, head looking down or at other people, it shows that person is not really engaged in the activity or person and may well prefer to be elsewhere.

Gestures – these are used to help to reinforce what is being or has been said to participants. For example, to help to ensure participants are running the right way round a sports hall, the sports leader can use their hand to point in the direction they should run.

Facial expressions – facial expressions help to reinforce what has been said. If a sports leader is impressed with a participant and the verbal feedback is positive then an appropriate facial expression such as a smile would be expected to go with this feedback, so the participant can see that the leader is pleased with their progress.

Demonstrations – a demonstration shows the participants how to perform a skill or technique. The sports leader needs to be able to show the participants what to do. The demonstration should be performed correctly so that participants do not learn incorrect techniques. On occasion, sports leaders may select a participant they know can perform the specific skill or technique appropriately to carry out the demonstration for the rest of the participants to see.

Eye contact – a sports leader should make eye contact with the participant they are communicating with. This helps the participant to know that the communication is directed at them and helps them to hold their attention and focus. This also allows a sports leader to see if the participant they are communicating with has understood what they have said.

Adapting communication style to meet the needs of different target groups – it is important for a leader to ensure their method of communication is appropriate for each target group. This may mean, for example, using very easy-to-understand terminology for young children with a soft tone of voice to try and help make the children feel at ease.

Active listening

While a sports leader needs to be sure that they can communicate effectively, they also need to actively listen to participants so that they can fully understand what it is the participant wants or needs. Active listening is a skill and involves the following principles:

- making eye contact with the participant – this shows that they have your full attention
- reacting to what the participant has said in an appropriate manner – such as nodding or verbally agreeing
- asking questions so that you can fully understand what the participant needs to know
- repeating back to the participant your understanding of what they want from you and asking them to confirm this. This is to ensure that the sports leader and participant leave the conversation satisfied that both know what the sports leader has been asked to do.

CHECK MY LEARNING

Describe why it is important for a sports leader to have good communication skills to be effective in their role.

Attributes of a leader: skills (2)

GETTING STARTED

Describe what sorts of things a sports leader needs to do before a session starts. Explain why it is important for a sports leader to get to their session early. What sorts of things do you think they need to check and are there any other reasons a sports leader should arrive early at their session?

Organisation

A successful leader needs to be organised and plan their sport or activity sessions, or ensure they understand the plan if they are using one that is already formulated.

Planning a session

As a sports leader you may be asked to plan a session and in so doing write a session plan. A session plan is a written plan which shows the structure of the session, including the timing of each activity, the activities to be used, how they should be set out, the resources required, etc., so it is a vital part of the planning stages of a sport or activity session. Part of the role may also require you to interpret a session plan that is written by another sports leader. As such, you will need to know what each part of a session plan should contain and what it means.

The first parts of a session plan are quite straightforward in relation to the information about the participants. The section that lists the activities and organisation of the activities should be written clearly so that any person using the session plan understands how the activity should be set out and what the participants should be doing.

Pre-session

◘ The sports leader needs to check and set up the equipment required before a session.

Collecting and checking equipment

A sports leader should collect their equipment prior to the session. The equipment will need to be checked and dealt with, such as putting goals up or pumping up balls, so that as soon as the participants arrive they are able to get started rather than wait for the sports leader to get everything ready. If equipment is damaged it shouldn't be used, so the sports leader will need to give themselves time to find alternative equipment for the session if necessary.

ACTIVITY

For a sport of your choice, make a list of all the equipment that is required for that sport and what sorts of checks and actions need to be carried out to ensure the equipment is suitable for use at an activity session.

The sports leader will need to check the facilities they are planning to use for the session. Part of this process may have involved booking the facility in advance. On arrival at the facility it should be risk-assessed by the sports leader to ensure there are no unexpected hazards. If any hazards are spotted that were not planned for in the risk assessment, the sports leader should have time to deal with these before the participants arrive. An example is wiping up spilt water on the floor.

The sports leader should also check that the facility is at the right temperature for the activity, which may involve adjusting the heating or air conditioning to bring the temperature to the right level before participants arrive. They may also need to open windows or a door in hot conditions so that participants don't overheat when taking part in the activity.

Post-session

Replacing equipment to appropriate area

Any equipment used will need to be checked to ensure it is not damaged and still in good working order, and then stored away. Some sports leaders will enlist the help of participants with this part of the session, which can help develop confidence in children as they may feel this is a position of responsibility and respond well to this request for help. The equipment then needs to be placed in its appropriate area.

Once the equipment has been checked and properly stored away, the sports leader should carry out an inspection of the facility to ensure it is in a fit state for the next people to use. This may involve picking up any dropped litter or mopping up any liquids from the floor from spilt drinks or perspiration.

CHECK MY LEARNING

List the activities a leader should complete pre-session and post-session, with descriptions of what each activity involves and why it should be carried out.

Attributes of a leader: skills (3)

The activity or sports leader needs to ensure that a planned session is structured for the time allowed. They should also ensure there is a progression of activities throughout the session, which will help to motivate the participants to keep taking part and to improve their physical health.

Activity structure

Progression through the session

Sport-specific session

The level of challenge and intensity of a physical activity session should increase throughout the session to motivate the participants to keep taking part. If participants are doing the same thing at the same level then they will not develop their skills if the session is sport-specific. Instead, the session should be planned so that the skill is developed by introducing new levels of challenge that become progressively more difficult. An example might be:

- introducing travel
- then introducing opposition
- followed by increasing the numbers of players in the drill, etc.

The progression should only be introduced when the participant is able to confidently complete the initial task.

Fitness improvement session

If the session is to improve fitness, then again, an increase in the intensity of the session should be incorporated into the session plan. The participants should have the opportunity to work as hard as they can so that the training is sufficient to lead to adaptations which will improve the component of fitness being trained.

Time frame

The sports leader should ensure the activity session runs to the time planned so that each part of the planned session has the time frame originally allocated. The activity session should finish on time as some participants may be being picked up by parents or carers, or may have somewhere else to get to after the session.

Motivation

During the session, the sports leader should ensure they continually motivate the participants using the various motivational methods which have been covered in Component 2.

Another way to motivate participants is to ensure that the planned activities are at the right level of intensity and challenge. They should be able to complete the planned activities and, if they cannot, then these activities should be adapted so that the participant is able to carry them out. For example, if a participant is not able to complete a full press-up then a half press-up can be given to them as an alternative. This helps to motivate the participants and prevent them from giving up and not completing the activity session.

Another method that can help to motivate participants is delegation. When a person is given a responsibility, they will often feel that they have been selected because the sports leader believes that they are good at performing that activity. This can improve a participant's self-confidence and motivation. For example, a person leading the session could ask a participant to identify an exercise that the whole group should complete, which allows them to choose something that they enjoy and can complete.

Knowledge of the activities being delivered

A key requirement for any person leading a sport or physical activity session is to have very good knowledge of the sport or physical activity that they are delivering. This allows the leader to:

- be able to see where participants are not performing a technique or exercise correctly and provide teaching points to support the participants to improve their performance or carry out the exercise safely and effectively
- provide adaptations to the planned activity to either make the activity more accessible for a person who may be having difficulty, or make the activity more difficult to challenge more able participants to help to maintain their motivation
- know what sorts of activities should be included in the warm-up and how to support participants to ensure they are carrying them out correctly. This helps to ensure participants are ready for the sport or activity session as well as reducing the chance of injury. The cool down helps participants to recover from a sport or activity session so is also an important component of the session.

It is very beneficial for a sports or activity leader to also be aware of any developments in technology that can be used in a sport or activity session. Technology can be used to help participants to get the best out of the session as well as to help track their progress.

- For example, if participants are wearing a smartwatch or a device that measures their heart rate, a leader could ask the participants to check how high their heart rate is after a particularly intense bit of exercise. They can then work out what training zone they are working in to ensure they are working at the targeted level.
- Other types of technology can help to add variety to a training session, for example spinning classes allow participants to race against each other in the class. This can also be motivational if a person sees that they are in the leading group.

■ Aerial yoga uses new technology to add variety to a yoga class, as well as support participants to achieve different positions to develop flexibility.

Attributes of a leader: skills (4)

After a sports or physical activity session, there is still work to do for the person leading the session in order to help them to develop their skills to become even more effective in their role.

It is important for a sports leader to evaluate the session and then set targets on how to improve their own planning and leading skills for future sessions. The development of the participants' skills in a sport or physical fitness will also need to be considered and should be thought about when planning the next activity session.

Evaluation

An evaluation is an honest review of how a sport or activity session went. The person that led the session can carry out a self-evaluation in which they consider what did and what didn't go well. They should base this on their observations of:

- how well the participants responded to the planned activities
- if they were able to complete them all
- if they looked like they were enjoying them, and
- if they looked like they were sufficiently challenged and engaged.

They should also consider what they did during the session to help and support the participants, such as one-to-one support for any participants who were not able to carry out the planned activity, as well as how they challenged the more able participants. They will need to consider their interaction with the whole group and if they thought all participants had a beneficial experience.

◻ The sports leader can carry out an evaluation with the participants to gain feedback.

During this process the evaluation should also consider things that did not go as planned, with reasons why this may be, as well as ways in which the sports leader can improve their planning and delivery of the session.

It is also possible for a sports leader to gain feedback from the participants and other people such as a mentor, to gain different perspectives on the sport or activity session. For example, some participants may not look like they are enjoying a session as they are working very hard, so they may appear to be unhappy or stressed. However, if they are asked afterwards they may say that they did enjoy the session as it really challenged them and that is what they wanted.

Target setting

Once an evaluation has been completed, a sports leader should always be able to find areas for development. The next step is to work out how to develop and improve your leadership skills based on this feedback; target setting can be used for this.

Target setting can be used both for the sports leader's development and also for the participants for whom they lead the session. The most popular method of setting targets is to use the SMART principles:

Specific

Measurable

Achievable

Realistic

Time-related

Specific – you need to state exactly what the target is. For example, rather than saying, 'I need to update my knowledge of netball', your target should be 'I need to improve my demonstrations for passing in netball'.

Measurable – how are you going to know if you have achieved the target? The target has to be something that you can measure to determine if you have met it. This could therefore be 'I will ask my teacher to watch each of my netball passes to check I am performing them properly'.

Achievable – the target that is set has to be something that you are able to complete.

Realistic – this is linked to achievable, which means you have to consider where you are now with the specific skill and how likely it is that you will be able to meet the target. For example, if an 18-year-old female has never played netball before and their target is to play for the county then this is probably not realistic.

Time-related – every target should have a time frame in which it is planned to have been met, usually over a few weeks or months, and then another target can be set.

Sports leader development

For some people, taking part in courses to help them to achieve set targets is a good idea. For example, if a person wanted to improve their skills in a certain sport they could take part in a course run by the National Governing Body (NGB) for that sport. Sports leaders who want to learn more about the rules for a specific sport could take a course for the first level of officiating for that sport (which again would be run by the NGB for that sport).

To find out about courses near you, go to the NGB website for the sport that you are interested in and have a look to see if they are running courses in your area.

There are lots of other ways that you can achieve your targets. Lots of practice is always beneficial, together with feedback so that you can continue to develop and improve.

Participant development

To help participants to achieve their targets it is important to know what the targets are to start with, and then work with the participants to set SMART targets. The sports leader is there to advise throughout each part of the SMART target setting process, especially when a participant is relatively new to the sport or activity as they may not know how quickly they can expect to progress. The sports leader can also then plan the sessions to take into account each participant's targets and work with them when the session is being delivered to help them to achieve their targets.

CHECK MY LEARNING

1 Discuss why it is important for a sports leader to carry out an evaluation after delivering a sport or activity session.

2 Explain what is meant by SMART targets.

3 Write out a SMART target that would be appropriate for:
   • a sports leader
   • a sports session participant.

Attributes of a leader: qualities (1)

GETTING STARTED

When you take part in a sports activity session, how are you encouraged to work hard and do your best? Does the sports leader use different methods to encourage you? Do you need any encouragement from a sports leader or is taking part in the sports activity sufficient encouragement for you to always do your best?

LINK IT UP

Extrinsic and intrinsic motivation is also discussed in Component 2: The impact of motivation on participation in sport and activity (pages 132–135).

Encouraging enthusiasm

Participants are not always initially keen to take part in a sport or activity session, as you may well know from experience. It is therefore vital that a sports leader is enthusiastic and keen at the start of the class to gear up the participants to be ready to enjoy the session. If the leader is smiling and looking like they are having fun, it will encourage participants to do the same. Being motivational is also important to help to support participants to try their hardest so that they get the best out of the sport or activity session.

Motivational techniques

When participants are learning new skills which they aren't able to perform properly or at all, or when they are having to exercise really hard and push themselves so that they are in some discomfort, many will feel like giving up. A good sports leader will need to use a range of methods to help to encourage these participants to keep trying so that they continue to participate in the activity session and reach their full potential – these encouragement methods are known as motivational techniques.

As we have seen in Component 2, motivation can be intrinsic and extrinsic.

Providing intrinsic motivational techniques

Intrinsic motivation must come from the person taking part in the sport or activity session, so it is not possible for a sports leader to provide this type of motivation in the same way that they can with extrinsic motivation. However, if the sports leader can plan and lead sessions so that they are fun and enjoyable, it will make the participants want to attend as they know they are going to have a good time. This will motivate them to make the time and effort to attend the sessions.

Ways to provide extrinsic motivational techniques

◻ Figure 3.1: Different types of extrinsic motivational techniques

Praise

When a participant has done something well, a sports leader should provide positive verbal or non-verbal feedback to confirm that they are performing the skill or technique appropriately or working hard, which will encourage them to repeat this performance. Examples of praise would be to say, 'Well done', 'Great effort' or 'Excellent, you've really got the hang of that technique!', or to smile or give them a thumbs-up.

Goal setting

This form of motivational technique involves the sports leader setting goals for an individual or group of participants. These goals should be both short-term and long-term and are put in place to help a person to progress. A short-term goal is something that a person can achieve in just a few weeks or even at the end of one activity session. A long-term goal is set over a longer period of time, such as a block of six weeks or a school term, for example.

Goal setting follows the same principles as target setting which has been covered in the skills section, in that they should be SMART goals.

ACTIVITY

Select a sport or activity that you take part in regularly. Write down a goal for yourself that meets the SMART principles.

Rewards

When participants work hard they often like to have some form of reward to recognise the effort and commitment that they have put in. Children in particular respond well to having some form of recognition in the form of a reward. Many sports leaders provide badges, stickers or certificates to participants to acknowledge hard work or achieving a certain skill or ability level.

ACTIVITY

Write down the different sports activities that you took part in when you were younger.

What forms of rewards were given out to participants during these sports?

How did receiving these awards make you feel?

Feedback

A sports leader should always try to give participants feedback on their performance so that each participant knows how well they are performing. Feedback can be positive to reinforce good practice. Where the sports leader wants to improve a specific aspect of performance, it is a good idea to tell the participant the good parts of what they are doing, followed by constructive feedback to help them to improve. For example, 'Well done, you are stepping into the pass correctly. Now turn your body so that you are side on to your partner when you throw the ball to them.'

CHECK MY LEARNING

1 Describe why it is important for a sports leader to use motivational techniques in order to be effective in their role.

2 Explain the different types of motivation you would use for the following participants:
   - a group of 14–16-year-old teenagers taking part in a football session
   - a gymnastics session for children aged 8–9 years old
   - an older adult taking part in a new sport.

Attributes of a leader: qualities (2)

Personality

An individual's personality is unique to themselves and is made up of many different factors. People can be described by aspects of their personality such as being sociable, relaxed or outgoing. Psychologists have provided different classifications for people's personality. These include extrovert and introvert and also type A and type B personalities. In both classifications, each category is virtually the complete opposite of the other; however, in reality, most people are somewhere in the middle of these two extremes.

Introvert and extrovert

An introvert is a person who is usually quite shy and quiet, and enjoys spending time on their own. They tend to keep their emotions to themselves and are reserved in large groups or with people they do not know very well. With people they do know well, they will usually be more relaxed and sociable.

An extrovert, however, likes to talk a lot, enjoys going out in groups and meeting new people, and likes being the centre of attention. However, they can be easily distracted and find it difficult if they are having to spend time on their own.

Type A and type B personalities

Type A personalities show traits of being self-critical and are more likely to get stressed and emotional. However, this type of personality is also more competitive and goal-oriented, has high levels of drive and is more focused. A type A personality hates to fail and will work very hard so that they don't fail.

☐ Type A personalities tend to be more competitive and goal-oriented but are more likely to be frustrated if the activity doesn't go well.

Type B personalities are generally more relaxed and calmer than type A personalities. This type of personality is tolerant and less competitive, as well as being less aggressive or likely to become frustrated by themselves or other people. They usually work steadily and enjoy doing well but are not stressed if they do not achieve all of their goals. However, they can be quite careless.

ACTIVITY

Explain which type of personality you think would enjoy the following types of sports or activities. Include reasons for your choice.

1 long-distance running
2 football
3 competitive swimming
4 circuit training
5 badminton.

Measuring personality

There are two questionnaires that are most commonly used to measure a person's personality: Eysenck's Personality Inventory (EPI) and the Profile of Mood States (POMS). Observing someone is another way to measure personality.

Inspiring confidence

The government provides regular advice and guidance related to the expectations of physical activity levels for people because participation in sport helps to keep people healthy. This means they are less likely to suffer from long-term illnesses such as diabetes and heart disease. Participation in regular activity has also been shown to help to improve a person's mental health by increasing their confidence and helping to reduce the risk of mental illnesses such as depression.

Both physical and mental health-related illnesses require substantial treatment and medication from the National Health Service (NHS) over time, which costs the NHS a lot of money. Therefore, preventing these types of illnesses is a good way for the government to save on NHS costs. A sports leader is key in helping people to meet these government targets by planning and delivering appropriate sport and activity sessions for different types of people and helping to motivate them to take part in regular sport and activity.

CHECK MY LEARNING

Locate a questionnaire to measure personality such as the Profile of Mood States (POMS). Complete the questionnaire and find out what personality type you are. Describe the results from the test and evaluate if you think they are accurate. If possible, check with a friend or family member to see what they think about the personality test results.

ACTIVITY

There are many health initiatives run by the national and local governments to try to increase participation in sport and physical activity.

Carry out research to describe one recent initiative to try and increase participation in sport and physical activity. Make sure you include the types of people the initiative is targeting and the methods it is using to try to increase participation.

Attributes of a leader: qualities (3)

There are a number of well-known sports leaders who have had different leadership styles yet still been very successful. For example, Jose Mourinho is a well-known football coach and manager who has led many top football teams. Charlotte Edwards, who was captain of the England women's cricket team, has been stated as being the epitome of good leadership.

ACTIVITY

Carry out research to find out about two different leaders in sport (one male and one female). Describe their involvement in the sport and what people have said about their leadership style.

There are three main types of leadership style:
- autocratic
- democratic
- laissez-faire.

Autocratic

◻ Alex Ferguson, who was manager of Manchester United football club, was a well-known and successful leader who used an autocratic approach.

An autocratic leadership style is one where a leader has total control and there is little input from any of the participants. It is used when an activity might contain potential hazards, or if the group is made up of young children. Autocratic leadership styles have both strengths and weaknesses.

Positives

The autocratic style of leadership can:
- be effective when decisions need to be made quickly and there is no time for discussion
- be effective when the leader clearly has the most knowledge and experience
- be beneficial in stressful situations where decisiveness is needed
- work well when everyone has very clear duties and responsibilities within a team
- be beneficial when working with a team who have high levels of personal motivation and want quick results
- be useful when dealing with challenging groups who need clear boundaries to be set.

Negatives

- Leaders might be seen as bossy or controlling.
- Ideas that other people have which may be useful to the entire group might be missed.
- It can be damaging to the sense of team within the group when the leader does not invite anyone else's thoughts.
- It discourages creative thinking or collaborative thinking.

ACTIVITY

Can you give an example of an autocratic leader? What is it about this leader which makes you believe they have an autocratic style?

Democratic

Democratic leadership is when a leader allows the entire group to have an input into decision-making. A captain of a sports team may have a democratic style.

Democratic leaders are in general considered to be good leaders, capable of getting positive outcomes from those they are responsible for. However, there are both positives and negatives associated with this style of leadership.

Positives

The democratic style of leadership can:
- encourage a sense of community in the team
- encourage creative and collaborative thinking, and nurture different ideas
- allow individuals to feel more involved in planning for their own success and therefore give them higher levels of motivation
- encourage trust among team members, which comes from a willingness to listen and take on board other people's ideas.

Negatives
- When the priority is a quick decision, time can be wasted during discussion.
- There can be a lot of trial and error as people's ideas are tested.
- When groups have little focus they can get easily sidetracked and struggle to stay on task.

ACTIVITY

Eleanor has a group of students that she is responsible for on a Wednesday afternoon. All of her students have had problems at school and either been expelled or suspended from mainstream classes. Eleanor has been asked to provide sessions that will give them focus and encourage teamwork and communication through sporting activity.

Her students do not enjoy a structured environment like the one at school. Some of them struggle with being told what to do. However, they are all still young and will benefit from being given some direction.

Eleanor decides to use a democratic style of leadership.

1 Why do you think Eleanor chooses a democratic style?

2 Do you think this will be effective?

3 Do you think that using a democratic style might lead to some challenges for her to overcome?

CHECK MY LEARNING

Explain three scenarios where:

1 an autocratic leadership style would be positive and help get the best out of a group

2 a democratic style might be the most effective leadership style to choose.

Attributes of a leader: qualities (4)

Laissez-faire

In laissez-faire leadership, the leader just supplies the resources the group needs, allowing the group to decide what they are going to do and how they are going to do it. This style of leadership is usually only suitable for individuals or groups that are very capable or do not require a great deal of support or direction. Laissez-faire leaders can be effective in the right setting or scenario. However, there are some negatives to this style which should also be considered.

Positives
- It can be beneficial when a team has a strong collective knowledge and are self-motivated.
- It might be useful when a group needs to look for alternative solutions to problems.

Negatives
- It is very reliant on a group being motivated and able to operate without any leadership.
- Leaders can be perceived to be disinterested or even lazy.
- Progress towards an end goal can be very slow without strong leadership keeping a group on track.

☐ A laissez-faire leader can be beneficial when a team are self-motivated but might be seen as disinterested.

ACTIVITY

Aaron has his first job as a teacher of physical education at a secondary school. He has a group of Year 9 students for the first time. He knows from other teachers that this class may sometimes be challenging and boisterous. However, in general they are popular with staff. Aaron chooses to use a laissez-faire style of leadership with them for his first class, which is taking part in fitness tests.

He brings worksheets and appropriate resources to class. He briefs the students and then sets them off to practise the tasks on the worksheet. Other than keeping an eye on the class so they remain safe, Aaron does not interrupt them until the end.

From the information given, explain if you think this fitness testing session would have been successful. Consider the following factors:

1 Would the children have learned how to administer (set up and carry out) a fitness test correctly?

2 Would the children have been able to record the fitness test results accurately?

3 Would the children know what component of fitness was being tested by each fitness test?

CHECK MY LEARNING

Complete Table 3.1 with the correct type of leadership style.

☐ **Table 3.1: Matching traits to a type of leadership style**

Leadership style	Leadership style traits
	Able to allow a team to learn from their own mistakes
	Draws on collaborative ideas and new thinking
	Is trusted and projects their own trust on the team
	Decisive when needed and capable of making a decision
	Can allow other leaders to emerge and take some responsibility
	Does not need other people's ideas to come up with a successful plan

The benefits of participation in sport and activity sessions: short-term physical

LINK IT UP

The benefits of regular participation in sport and activity are also covered in Component 1: Physiological impact of engagement in sport and activity on the body systems (pages 12–13).

When we take part in sport and activity our body needs to get oxygen and nutrients to the working muscles. We also need to be able to perform a range of different types of movements compared with when we are at rest. To do this there are a variety of short-term responses that our body systems will undergo in a sport or activity session.

Increased blood flow to the working muscles

When we are at rest, blood is flowing to various parts of our body, with more blood flowing to areas such as the digestive system after we have eaten a meal or a snack. However, as soon as we start to take part in any form of exercise, less blood will be directed to areas like the digestive system and more blood flow will be directed to the working muscles. This is because the working muscles need this increased blood flow to supply them with oxygen and nutrients, as well as to remove waste products that are produced when muscles are working.

ACTIVITY

For the following sports and activities, identify which muscle groups are working and give reasons why they would require an increased blood flow to them:

1 cycling
2 swimming front crawl
3 tennis.

Increased muscle temperature

The process of muscle contraction creates movement. This process also releases heat energy which has the effect of increasing the temperature of the muscles. This helps to increase the pliability of the muscles. It also has the effect of increasing the body temperature, so we respond by sweating to try and reduce the body temperature.

Increased range of movement at a joint

Joints that allow movement are called synovial joints. These joints have a fluid between them called synovial fluid which is there to help to lubricate the joint to allow it to move more freely. Taking part in sport has the effect of increasing the amount of synovial fluid released into a synovial joint. This helps to increase the range of movement permitted at a joint.

◘ **It is important to warm up before taking part in a sport or activity.**

Increased heart rate

You will no doubt have experienced the effect that taking part in sport or activity has on your heart rate. Your heart rate is the number of times your heart contracts. Each time your heart contracts it pumps blood out of it. The more times it contracts, the more blood is being pumped around your body.

An increased heart rate has the effect of improving the delivery of oxygen to the working muscles so they can use this to provide energy for them to contract. This increased heart rate means more blood is being pumped around the body to transport and take away waste materials from the working muscles such as carbon dioxide and lactic acid. If these waste products were not removed they would quickly stop the muscles from being able to contract.

The cool down

At the end of a sport or activity session it is important to take part in a cool down activity/exercise, as this aids in the removal of lactic acid from working muscles. A cool down also decreases the heart rate, allowing the cardiorespiratory system to return to its resting state. This is covered in much more detail later on in the component.

CHECK MY LEARNING

Explain the short-term physical benefits of taking part in sport and activity sessions.

The benefits of participation in sport and activity sessions: long-term physical (1)

Participants of all ages will benefit from increased fitness levels from regular participation in sport and physical activity. Increased fitness levels will then allow a person to get better at a particular sport as they can concentrate on learning the techniques rather than feeling uncomfortable as they are struggling to keep on going. Increased fitness levels will help people to go about their everyday life, such as walking to the shops and carrying heavy shopping bags. There are a range of long-term benefits which will be beneficial to a person's health and reduce the likelihood of them suffering from certain diseases that are associated with not taking part in regular sport and activity.

ACTIVITY

Machines, devices and gadgets are now in place in the modern world so that the amount of physical activity a person has to do to complete everyday activities is reduced; for example washing machines are now used rather than hand washing clothes.

1 Make a list of all the machines, devices and gadgets you are aware of that reduce the amount of physical activity a person has to do on a daily basis.

2 Give reasons for how each of these machines, devices and gadgets can lead to a reduction in physical activity on a daily basis.

Cardiorespiratory benefits

Reduced risk of type 2 diabetes

Diabetes is a disease that stops a person from being able to regulate their blood sugar levels. This is because their body is either not producing any, or sufficient quantities, of a hormone called insulin. Insulin is produced by the pancreas and is released when blood sugar levels rise, which usually happens after a person has eaten something sugary or after they have eaten a meal.

- Type 1 diabetes usually occurs in children and the cause of this disease is still not fully known. In this situation, the pancreas stops producing insulin.
- Type 2 diabetes, however, is a disease which usually occurs in adults and older adults, and is mainly brought on from eating a diet high in sugar, and not taking part in regular sport and physical activity.

For people with mild type 2 diabetes, a change in diet and participation in regular sport and physical activity can prevent the need for medical intervention, as the body cells have improved sensitivity to insulin and are more able to react when insulin is released to decrease the levels of glucose in the bloodstream. For more severe type 2 diabetes, insulin may need to be prescribed but dietary changes and participation in regular sport and physical activity have been shown to have a positive impact.

In the UK, about 90 per cent of people with diabetes have type 2 diabetes. Currently, over 4 million people in the UK are estimated to have diabetes, which is forecast to increase to 5 million in 2025.

Explain three reasons why you think type 2 diabetes is increasing in the UK.

Reduced risk of hypertension

Hypertension is also known as high blood pressure and is harmful to a person's health. The following conditions have been linked to hypertension:

- coronary heart disease (CHD)
- stroke
- heart attack.

CHD is where the blood vessels that supply the heart muscle itself become clogged up and reduce blood flow to the heart. This can lead to heart conditions such as **angina** or even a **heart attack**.

A heart attack is where the blood supply to the heart is totally blocked, so the heart is not receiving enough oxygen and nutrients and is no longer able to contract. If the heart is no longer able to contract, blood will not be pumped around the body. A heart attack will often result in death; however, medical advances mean that more and more people are now able to recover from a heart attack if they receive swift and appropriate medical treatment.

CHD is a condition that usually only occurs in middle age or older, so adults and older adults would benefit most from ensuring they continue to take part in regular aerobic sport and physical activities. Aerobic sport and physical activities include swimming, jogging and cycling for periods of 20 minutes or longer, and should be carried out at least three times per week to help improve cardiovascular fitness and reduce the risk of CHD. As the heart is a muscle, it responds to aerobic exercise by getting larger and stronger, which means it can work more efficiently. Exercise increases the number of blood vessels supplying the heart and muscles with blood, which increases the supply of nutrients and oxygen to the working muscles and helps to reduce blood pressure.

Strokes are also linked to hypertension. A stroke is where the blood supply to the brain is cut off. Strokes can result in death or long-term problems caused by injury to the brain such as reduced movement, problems with speech, weakness or **spasticity** in muscles.

Carry out research to find out about one method of medical intervention to treat a person who has suffered, or is suffering, from a heart attack. Write a description of this method and how it helps the person to recover from a heart attack.

Regular participation in aerobic sports or physical activities decreases resting blood pressure because it reduces blood viscosity due to an increase in blood plasma. Doctors will often 'prescribe' regular participation in aerobic sport and/or physical activity to help reduce blood pressure, where appropriate for the individual.

Hypertension means high blood pressure.

Angina is chest pain or discomfort due to reduced blood flow to the heart muscle.

A **heart attack** can happen when blood flow to the heart muscle is stopped and the heart muscle tissue begins to die.

Heart attack symptoms can differ between men and women. Apart from the more well-known symptoms such as pain and tightness in the chest, women are more likely to experience pain or discomfort between the shoulder blades, dizziness and/or nausea, feeling weak and indigestion-like pain.

Spasticity is where muscles become very stiff and tight, which results in them being able to perform very restricted movements.

Produce a poster to encourage people to take part in regular aerobic sport and/or physical activity by highlighting the cardiorespiratory benefits of participation.

The benefits of participation in sport and activity sessions: long-term physical (2)

GETTING STARTED

Describe one adaption of the musculoskeletal system to regular weight bearing or resistance sports and/or physical activities.

As part of a healthy exercise programme, people are encouraged to take part in regular resistance sports or activities to improve the health of their muscular and skeletal systems. Flexibility training is also important for health and well-being, as well as sporting performance.

Musculoskeletal benefits

The musculoskeletal system consists of the muscular system and skeletal system. Weight bearing exercises such as jogging or playing netball, and resistance exercises such as using bodyweight, free weights or resistance machines, will help to produce benefits to these body systems.

Reduced risk of osteoporosis

Osteoporosis is a disease in which the mineral density of bones is decreased, resulting in the bones becoming fragile and more likely to break. Women are four times more likely than men to develop this disease. Osteoporosis is preventable for many people by eating a healthy diet with the recommended daily amount of calcium and vitamin D, as well as taking part in regular weight bearing and/or resistance sports or physical activities.

Prevention is very important because although there are treatments for osteoporosis, there is currently no cure. If a person has exercised regularly in childhood and adolescence, they are more likely to build strong, dense bones, which will stand them in good stead for the rest of their life.

DID YOU KNOW?

Your bones are continually renewing themselves through a process called bone remodelling, where old bone cells are destroyed and new bone cells are formed. It has been estimated that your whole skeleton regenerates every 10 years. However, age, gender and lifestyle will affect how long it actually takes each individual to renew their skeleton.

ACTIVITY

Identify appropriate weight bearing or resistance sports or activities for the following people, with reasons for each choice:

1 14-year-old male
2 55-year-old male
3 72-year-old female.

Reduced risk of joint injury

The strength of ligaments and tendons increases in response to regular participation in weight bearing and resistance sports and physical activities. This means joints are stronger and more able to withstand forces, so are less likely to be injured. For example, a person who regularly takes part in cross-country running, which is a weight bearing exercise, will have developed strong ligaments around their ankles. This means they are less likely to sprain their ankle when running over uneven ground.

ACTIVITY

Describe a joint injury either you or a sports person you have seen in the media has suffered from. Identify the location of the joint injury and describe how it occurred.

Reduced risk of poor posture through increased strength of core

Many people have a slouched body posture where their shoulders are forwards, stomach is relaxed and the upper back is arched. This can lead to several health problems such as back pain, migraines and an increased risk in **slipping a disc** in the back. A good posture is where the shoulders are back, the back is straight, and the head is looking forwards. Posture can be improved through resistance exercises that focus on the abdominals, back muscles and pelvis.

KEY TERM

Slipped disc – a disc is positioned between each vertebra in the spine to act as a shock absorber. If the disc slips, it moves out of its correct position and can press on nerves in the spine which can cause numbness or pain along the affected nerve.

■ Figure 3.2: Poor posture can lead to health problems such as back pain and migraines

Improved flexibility

Flexibility is the range of movement available at a joint – the more flexible a person is, the greater the range of movement at their joints. For example, a gymnast performing the splits has a large range of movement in their hip joint.

Some flexibility is required for normal everyday living, such as reaching up to the top of a cupboard to take down a jar of food, and in sporting activities, such as lunging for a shot in badminton. If a person is not flexible or has very limited flexibility, they are more prone to injuries such as straining a muscle.

CHECK MY LEARNING

The following exercise classes have become very popular over the last few years:

yoga   Pilates   Body Pump™

Carry out research to find out what is involved in each of these exercise classes and describe how each class produces health benefits to the participants.

The benefits of participation in sport and activity sessions: psychological

Psychological health benefits

Participation in sport and physical activity can have a positive impact on a person's psychological health. We are all aware of the physical benefits of regular participation in sport and activity; however, more and more research is showing there is a significant psychological benefit too.

Increased intrinsic motivation to continue participation

The more a person takes part in sport and activities, the greater the intrinsic motivation to continue their participation. Initially, some people may have taken part in sport or an activity as they were encouraged to from extrinsic rewards such as trying to lose weight or wanting to play well to win a medal or gain recognition in a sporting event. However, the more a person participates, the greater the intrinsic motivation will be, as participation becomes something that they enjoy rather than them hoping to achieve any additional external gains.

Improved concentration and effort in the session

The more a participant attends sport and activity sessions, the more likely they will be able to focus on what is being covered in the session, as they will know what their own limits are and how their body will respond to specific sport and activity demands. They can then put in more effort so that they can try and do even better in the session, which will lead to improvements in the sport or to fitness level development.

Increased motivation, ensuring that intensity of effort during participation is higher

When a participant has attended a number of sessions, they will have developed their fitness levels and techniques for the selected sport or activity. They will then have higher levels of motivation as they will often have set goals for what they want to achieve during each session and over a period of time. This will help participants to work at a high intensity and put in as much effort as possible, as they know what to expect from the session. They will therefore be able to pace themselves so that they are putting in high levels of effort that can be sustained for the duration of the session.

Extrinsic motivation provided by the leader

Many participants will develop a rapport with the sport or activity leader and continue to attend sessions as they enjoy the leader's training methods and also the extrinsic rewards that they provide. For young children these rewards may be stickers for putting in a lot of effort. For adults the reward may simply be praise, stating they have done well to complete a specific exercise, having observed previously that they were not able to achieve it. An example is someone being able to complete full press-ups at a circuit station rather than having to drop to their knees for the last half of the time at the station.

Release of serotonin and endorphins

When people take part in sport and physical activity their body releases endorphins and serotonin. These endorphins and serotonin help to relieve feelings of pain that may be felt while exercising, and have the added benefit of improving mood – this is sometimes known as 'the runner's high'. In cases of mild depression, exercise participation may be prescribed by a GP to boost a patient's mood.

Depression is something that does not usually occur in primary school-aged children but can be something that teenagers, adults or older adults may suffer from, so it is important that these participant age groups take part in regular sport and physical activity to try and reduce the risk of depression.

Increased self-confidence

Taking part in regular sport and physical activity can help to improve a person's self-confidence. This can result from the feeling gained from being good at a particular sport and then achieving fitness goals, such as running a half-marathon or learning new basketball skills, which will leave people feeling confident in their own abilities.

For beginners, completing their first sport or activity session can be a huge self-confidence boost, as they may not have felt they were able to complete the session or were not up to the same standard as the other participants. This could then help that participant continue to take part in sport and activity sessions in the future.

Taking part in outdoor sports activities such as rock climbing or abseiling can help to build people's confidence, as these types of activities take a person outside of their comfort zone and positively challenge them. These sorts of activities are perceived as dangerous and those taking part in them will usually feel afraid, sometimes to the point where they may almost fear for their life. However, with all the safety precautions in place, these fears are usually unfounded. By completing an activity that is seen as challenging and dangerous, people will feel pleased and proud for overcoming their fear, and this can lead to an increase in confidence.

◨ Taking part in rock climbing can help to improve self-confidence.

ACTIVITY

Think about sports and physical activities that you have taken part in and currently take part in. Explain how each one has supported you to build your self-confidence, as well as any that have not had such a positive influence on your self-confidence. Also consider what other sorts of sports you could take part in which would help to further improve your self-confidence and self-esteem.

CHECK MY LEARNING

Produce a leaflet that could be handed out to people at a sport or health and fitness centre to describe the psychological benefits of taking part in sport and activity.

Learning aim A: assessment practice

How you will be assessed

Now that you have studied the topics in learning aim A you will need to show that you understand the key requirements of sport and activity leadership, including the skills and qualities of a leader. You also need to know why it is important to provide sport and activity sessions in relation to the physical short- and long-term benefits, as well as the psychological benefits.

CHECKPOINT

Strengthen

- Explain how the skills and qualities of a sports leader help them support participants in a sport or activity session.
- Explain the different personality types and their effect on sports leadership.
- Assess the different leadership styles and their contribution to being a successful sports leader.
- Outline the physical and psychological benefits of participation in sport and activity sessions.

Challenge

- Assess ways in which a sports leader can demonstrate the required skills and qualities to be a successful sports leader.
- Explore the advantages and disadvantages of a sports leader's skills and qualities.
- Give justified reasons how a sports leader can promote physical and psychological benefits of participation in sport and activity for a specific target group.

ASSESSMENT ACTIVITY LEARNING AIM A

Attend a sport or activity session and observe the sports leader as they are taking the session.

1 While completing your observation, make notes on the following skills used by the sports leader:

- types of communication used
- listening skills
- organisation
- activity structure
- knowledge of the activities
- target setting.

You should explore how the sports leader uses each skill and how the participants react.

2 Write an overview of the sports leader's skills that assesses if some skills are used in a more effective way than others and if some skills could be improved on.

3 You should also explore the qualities of the sports leader. Make a note of the following while observing the sports leader:

- their enthusiasm and how they encourage participants to be enthusiastic
- how they encourage intrinsic motivation
- how they use extrinsic motivation
- if they inspire confidence
- what sort of personality you think they are
- what leadership style they use.

4 Again, write an overview which assesses each of these qualities and if some of the qualities are used more successfully than others.

While observing, try and note if the sports leader provides any support or information to the participants about the physical benefits and psychological benefits of taking part in regular sport and activity sessions.

5 Prepare a leaflet that could be handed out to participants to let them know about the short- and long-term physical benefits of participation, as well as the psychological benefits of participation.

TIPS

It is not always possible to see if a sports leader is developing intrinsic motivation in the participants because during a strenuous activity session, the participants may not look like they are enjoying themselves as they are working so hard. Therefore, it may be an idea to prepare a questionnaire for them to complete after the session to find out what they thought about the activity session. This will give you a much better idea about how successful the sports leader was in leading their activity session.

TAKE IT FURTHER

Write a report to review how the target group taking part in the observed sport or physical activity session would gain specific benefits both physically and psychologically, and ways in which regular participation could be encouraged for that particular target group.

Target groups: children and young people

Different groups of people may have different reasons for taking part in sport and physical activity. They may also have some reasons for not taking part in sport and physical activity. If we know each of these reasons we can try to improve provision for specific groups so that they are more likely to participate in physical activity, and therefore help to improve their physical health. In addition, understanding why specific groups don't take part in regular or any physical activity can help to provide ideas and initiatives to reduce barriers to participation.

Specific groups of people are referred to as target groups. You will need to know the reasons for participation and non-participation for each of the following target groups:

- children and young people
- people with disabilities
- older people
- people from particular ethnic groups
- women
- LGBTI – lesbian, gay, bisexual, transgender and intersex.

Children

Children are supposed to be active for 60 minutes a day. It is important that they enjoy taking part in sport so that they can easily meet this minimum time requirement.

Most children respond well to sports that are fun. Also, their age will determine how much of the sport should have a 'make-believe element' and how much should replicate 'grown-up' sport. Most children will be beginners and still need to master many of the basic skills in sport, which include catching, throwing, running, jumping and kicking.

As they get older they are able to combine these skills, so by the age of 11 most children will have all the skills they need to play a game of netball or football. At this age, males and females will usually compete against each other, rather than take part in single-sex sports.

ACTIVITY

For a group of children aged between 4 and 7 and between 8 and 11, make two different lists of sports that you think would be appropriate for each age group. Give reasons why you think they would be appropriate.

Young children have lots of energy but only in short bursts – therefore, children would not enjoy anything that requires high levels of endurance over the same time as an adult activity, such as a football match, for example, which would usually be 90 minutes long. For children, a full game should be much shorter than this. Children also do not have well-developed methods of thermoregulation, so they can overheat very quickly. Therefore, lots of breaks to cool down and rehydrate should be taken when primary school-aged children take part in sport and physical activity in a warm environment.

Young people

Young people are classed as aged between 14 and 18. They will range quite widely in their ability levels. Some will have played a specific sport for some time and will be playing at a high level, and there may also be some sports that they have never taken part in.

Think about the sports that you take part in with your friends. List any sports where the group are of the same ability level and also sports where ability levels differ within the group.

Many young people will have improved their coordination and ability to perform the basic techniques required to take part in a range of different sports. Within the group there will be some young people who are very good at a specific sport, usually one that they have played since primary school. If a person is running a sports activity session, this range in ability can sometimes make it difficult to run a successful session. So in these cases, some sports leaders choose sports that are not as familiar to the whole group, such as volleyball, which is something that not many teenagers will have played at primary school. Therefore, all participants are at the beginner ability level.

Other new sports and physical activities, such as footgolf and pickleball, are continually being developed. Some young people may like to take part in newer 'trendy' sports or physical activities as they may feel these are more appropriate to their age group.

■ New sports, such as footgolf, can provide an activity session where no one has the advantage of much previous experience of the sport.

Young people can also be quite self-conscious when taking part in sport so may try to avoid participating in sports that they feel they are not very good at.

At this age, males and females will usually take part in single-sex sports, as males will often be bigger than females, which can make sports such as contact sports dangerous if played in a mixed group. However, some sports can be played by both males and females. In these situations, the sport played should not have any contact and differences in gender-related fitness should not play a significant role in the potential outcome. Examples of suitable sports would be badminton, volleyball and rounders.

For a male or female young person, explain a choice of sport that you would recommend to encourage the young person to take part in, giving reasons for your choice.

Target groups: people with disabilities

There are many different types of disabilities. It is important that you have some understanding of the differences, as each will have an impact on the types of sports a participant is able to take part in and impact on their reasons for participation and non-participation.

People with disabilities

Disability broadly falls into three categories:
- visual
- hearing
- physical.

People may be born with any of these disabilities or the disability may occur later on in life from an accident or illness.
- Visual – a person with a visual disability may have a decreased ability to see, which is not corrected by wearing glasses. A person with a visual disability may be able to make out some objects or may be totally blind.
- Hearing – a person with a hearing disability may be able to hear some limited sound or not hear at all.
- Physical – physical disabilities come in many different categories, depending on which area of the body is affected. The list below provides some types of physical disability that you should be aware of:
  - Spinal cord injury – an injury to the spinal cord will result in loss of function of specific parts of the body, depending on the location of the spinal cord injury. People with this physical disability will require crutches or a wheelchair.
  - Paraplegia – a person with paraplegia has loss of function to their legs and the lower part of their body.

◻ Marc McCarroll has a spinal cord injury and plays wheelchair tennis for Great Britain.

- Tetraplegia – a person with tetraplegia has total or partial impairment of function of their legs and arms.
- Loss or deformity of limbs – a person with this type of physical disability may have an artificial limb.
- Cerebral palsy – this condition is as a result of damage to the brain which decreases motor function. A person with this condition will usually have movement and coordination problems.

Initially, a person may require support and guidance to cope with a new disability as well as learn a new sport. They may not be able to take part in the sport in its original format due to their disability. A person with a long-term disability will need to have access to equipment, coaches and centres that are able to run sports that are suitable for a person with disabilities. There has been significant improvement over the years in relation to provision of sports for a person with disabilities.

ACTIVITY

A range of sports and adapted sports are available for people with disabilities to take part in.

Carry out research to complete the table about each of the sports shown below.

Sport	Description of sport or activity	Description of how a person or team wins
Boccia		
Goalball		
Sledge hockey		
Handcycling		
Blind golf		
Sitting volleyball		

CHECK MY LEARNING

Carry out research to find out about the different classifications of disability that people can compete in for a disability sporting event of your choice.

Target groups: older people

The number of older people in the population is growing as people are living longer. Many older adults are much fitter and stronger than in previous generations. This is due to better nutrition, health care and regular participation in sport and physical activity.

Older people

Types of sport appropriate for older people

As people get older, fitness starts to decline. Some older adults may have health concerns which will impact on the types of sports that they can take part in. However, research strongly suggests that participation in appropriate sport and physical activities is beneficial for an older adult's health and well-being.

Many older adults will experience issues with their joints from wear and tear over the years. In these instances, sports and physical activities that involve **high impact** movements are not appropriate as these place extra stress on the joints.

Low impact sports are therefore usually the most appropriate activity for older adults.

Activities in water, such as an aqua-aerobics session, are low impact.

As people get older they may experience cardiovascular health concerns such as high blood pressure. In these instances, **high intensity** sports may raise their blood pressure too much and are therefore not appropriate.

Older people have a range of potential health concerns that their body may be experiencing through the ageing process. As people get older, their bones may become more fragile and so are more likely to fracture on impact compared with younger people. This means any form of contact sport is generally not recommended for an older adult. For some older adults, even standing for long periods of time may be difficult or cause discomfort, so exercise programmes that can be carried out while sitting down have been devised to help keep older adults active without posing a threat to their health and well-being.

Some types of sports may be low impact and **low intensity** but are still not appropriate for the older adult, such as an outdoor pursuits type of activity which has an element of risk or potential discomfort. For example, kayaking can be performed at a low intensity, but if the boat capsized the older adult may be frightened and exposed to very cold water, which could raise their heart rate to a high level and put their health at risk.

CHECK MY LEARNING

Carry out research to find out about low impact and low intensity types of sports and activities. If you were advising a leisure centre that wanted to increase the participation of older adults in sport and activity in their local area, what types of sports and physical activities would you recommend? Explain your choices, giving reasons why each selected sport and activity is appropriate for older adults.

KEY TERMS

High intensity involves taking part in an activity that raises your heart rate to a high level, such as cycling at a very fast rate or up a steep hill.

Low intensity involves an activity that raises your heart rate to a low-to-moderate level, such as walking.

Target groups: ethnic groups, women and LGBTI

People from particular ethnic groups

Certain aspects of culture or religion may restrict the activities that people from some ethnic groups feel they are able to take part in. In some cases, the clothing that is usually worn to participate in a specific sport may restrict some cultures from being able to participate, such as a male who wears a turban as part of their Sikh religion. This may result in issues with horse riding, where health and safety requires a safety helmet to be worn and therefore potentially requires the removal of the turban.

Some sport and active leisure sessions are able to take these aspects into account. For example, some religions require women to be fully covered while in the presence of males. This means swimming wearing a traditional swimsuit is not permissible. However, swimming costumes are now available that fully cover the body and hair. In addition, some leisure centres run female-only swimming sessions, with only females permitted to swim and female lifeguards on duty.

Some religions require a person to pray at specific times of the day. To help to support this religious requirement some leisure centres have a prayer room, which can help people to participate in sport and activity and then be able to take part in their prayers without having to leave the centre.

◘ Swimming costumes that cover the full body and hair are now available.

ACTIVITY

Visit your local sport or leisure centre. Find out how this centre caters for people from particular ethnic groups. Does it run specific sessions for people from ethnic groups? Look at the people using the centre. Are a range of ethnic groups represented at the sport or leisure centre? Write up your findings in a report.

Women

Research shows that there are significantly more males taking part in regular sport and physical activity compared to females – research to date suggests up to 2 million more 14–40-year-old males than females. There are many reasons why this is the case, including:

- fear of judgement on appearance when taking part in sport or afterwards
- fear of judgement on ability levels – some women are worried they do not have the ability to take part in sport or physical activity
- family commitments – looking after young children
- lack of access – the types of sports and physical activities that women enjoy are not available to them.

ACTIVITY

Make a list of sports and physical activities that are available for males and another list of what is available for females in your local area. Do you notice a difference in the provision of sport and activity between males and females?

A number of campaigns have been run to help to support women to take part in sport and to overcome any concerns they may have about participation. 'This Girl Can' is an example of such a campaign.

◘ Campaigns such as 'This Girl Can' help to encourage more females to take part in sport and physical activities.

LGBTI

LGBTI stands for lesbian, gay, bisexual, **transgender** and **intersex**. People in this target group may have had to deal with various prejudices and a lack of an inclusive approach to participation in sport and physical activity. This has meant a number of people in this target group have given up on sport or hidden their sexuality or gender identity. Language has been used in sport that is **homophobic** and **transphobic**, in some cases as a form of 'banter' — another reason why participation is lower in LGBTI groups than expected.

KEY TERMS

Transgender means a person who does not identify with their birth sex.

Intersex means a person born with both male and female sex characteristics.

Homophobic describes a form of prejudice against homosexual people.

Transphobic describes a form of prejudice against transgender people.

CHECK MY LEARNING

Carry out research into campaigns or events that help to increase participation in sport and activity for the following target groups:

1 people from particular ethnic groups

2 women

3 people who identify as LGBTI.

Explain how each campaign or event is attempting to increase participation for each target group, exploring any barriers to participation for each group and ways the campaign is trying to overcome these.

ACTIVITY

LGBTI people are not represented well in high-level sport on the whole. Make a list of sports people competing at a high level who are part of the LGBTI group. Explain if you notice any sports that appear to be better represented by LGBTI individuals compared to other sports. Explain why you think some sports have better representation than others.

Types of sessions

There are many different types of physical activity sessions but they can broadly be placed into the following categories:

- fitness
- sport
- multi-activity.

Fitness

These sessions aim to help to improve a person's fitness and are often focused on enabling a person to meet their specific goal, for example trying to lose weight, or to increase fitness so that they can take part in a specific sporting goal, such as running a half-marathon.

There is a huge variety of fitness sessions, which means they are available for all types of people of all abilities. For example, aqua aerobics is a fitness class that takes place in water. This means there is less impact on the joints as the exercise is all low impact. This makes the class suitable for older participants who may have joint concerns. It is also suitable for any person who is obese: the water helps to provide buoyancy which means people's legs are not having to bear their full weight, so the water helps to reduce the impact of any activity they are taking part in. Some fitness classes incorporate dance moves, such as Zumba, which women may find appealing, whereas other fitness sessions can include boxing moves, such as Boxercise, which appeals to both males and females.

Sport

Sport sessions are used to develop skills and techniques for participants so that they are able to take part in a particular sport in a competitive or non-competitive environment.

Team sports

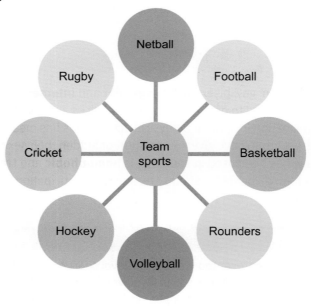

◻ Figure 3.3: Examples of sports played in teams

A team sport is where two or more players are working together against two or more people on an opposing team.

There are a great range of team sports available. Some are played mainly by one gender in schools but most sports can be played by both males and females. In competition, however, most team sports will involve males competing against males and females competing against females.

Individual sports

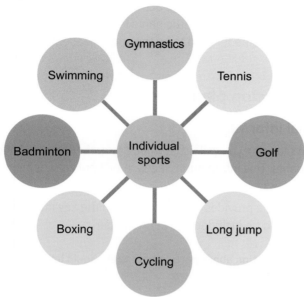

□ **Figure 3.4: Examples of sports played by individuals**

An individual sport is where one person is competing against one other person, for instance in tennis. The person may be judged on their performance, such as in gymnastics, and their scores are compared to other competitors to determine the places achieved in the event.

ACTIVITY

Carry out research to find out what other types of team and individual sports are available which are not included in Figures 3.3 and 3.4.

Outdoor activities such as kayaking, sailing and orienteering are sports that can be included in team sports or individual sports, depending on the nature of the activity.

Multi-activity

These types of sessions include lots of different types of activities to help to prevent boredom and engage all participants in physical activity. Multi-activity sessions are very popular with children and young people who would usually find doing the same thing for a long period of time quite tedious, as this target group can have a short attention span. These sessions include fitness and sports, and each activity will last around 30 minutes or less. Many children do multi-activity sessions over the holiday period, which involves taking part in a range of different sports. This helps them to learn new techniques and is a good introduction to playing a range of sports.

CHECK MY LEARNING ■ ■

Compare and contrast a fitness session, a sport session and a multi-activity session.

Explain suitable fitness, sport sessions and/or multi-activity sessions for the following target groups:

1 children and young people
2 people with disabilities
3 people from a particular ethnic background
4 women
5 people who identify as LGBTI
6 older people.

Session plan

When planning an activity session, it is important that a session plan is written out. A session plan template can be used to help ensure the session plan contains all of the information that needs to be considered when planning an activity session. It can also include a time schedule for each activity that is planned. The session plan contains key information about the participants for whom the sports activity session is being planned. This can be referred to by the sports leader before and during the activity session.

First part of session planning

Use of personal information

As part of session planning you will usually need to gather personal information about the participants. This information needs to be kept confidential so that no other person is able to access it.

The template in Table 3.2 provides sections to add in the key information about participants that should be included in a session plan.

 Table 3.2: Key information about participants that should be in a session plan

Aim of the sport or activity session				
About the participants				
Age range:		Number of participants:		
	Number of males:		Number of females:	
Are there any participants with special educational needs and disabilities (SEND)? If yes, please give details.				
Ability of the participants:				

Aims of the session

It is important for every activity session to have specific **aims** – these can only really be devised once the sport and ability of the participants is known. The aims should therefore be set to meet the needs of the chosen target group. When the person leading the session has selected an appropriate sport for a group of participants and knows their ability range, they can work out what the aims of the session should be.

An aim is essentially what the person leading the event wants the participants to get out of the session and achieve after having taken part in it. It is important that the targets set are realistic for each group so that each participant has the ability to achieve the expected outcome.

An example of an aim is: Each participant should be able to perform a chest pass, bounce pass and overarm pass in netball.

For a sport of your choice, write down suitable aims for a group of participants aged 14–16 of beginner ability level.

Participants

During your planning, you will need to consider a range of different aspects about the participants, including age, gender, numbers, and medical and special needs.

Age

The age of sports participants is a very important factor, as a session that would be appropriate for a group of 18 year olds would not be suitable for a group of 8 year olds. The younger the age group, the simpler the activity needs to be. You will also need to take into account the fact that you will need a higher number of helpers when working with younger children. With older participants, such as teenagers or adults, you may find you don't need any helpers.

Explain what sort of activity session you would plan for the following groups of participants:

1 6-year-old males and females
2 14-year-old girls
3 60–70-year-old males and females

Give reasons for each of your selected activity sessions that show that the age of the participant has been taken into consideration.

Gender

The gender of the participants is important when deciding whether sports are appropriate for a mixed group. This is not necessary for younger children as mixed gender groups are fine. However, as the children get older, contact sports are not appropriate. It is also a good idea to find out the number of males and females taking part in the sports activity session, as this may have an impact on the choice of sport that would be most appropriate for the group.

Some activities such as netball tend to be played only by females. If the participants are both male and female, then it is usually better to choose an activity that can appeal to both and does not involve contact, such as volleyball or badminton.

Number of participants

The number of participants will help to determine what sort of sports session you plan. You should always try to make sure that all the participants are actively involved in the session for the majority of the time. Participants who have to sit and watch are more likely to become bored, which often leads to misbehaviour in children and young people, and adults becoming distracted and finding other activities to entertain themselves.

Medical and special needs

It is important to know of any medical or special needs that participants may have. A good way for a leader to know the medical backgrounds of the participants is to ask them to complete documentation before taking part. Examples of appropriate documentation are shown later in the component.

Explain what type of sports session you would choose for the following group of participants:

1 age: 12–14
2 number and gender: 24 – 10 females, 14 males
3 medical or special needs: one participant has a hearing impairment
4 ability: mixed

Include reasons about how your selected sport would be appropriate for this group.

Session plan: first part of session planning (1)

Resources

Resources include the facility, location, equipment and clothing.

Facility and location

A facility could be a sports hall, a swimming pool or a gym, and a location could be a playing field or tennis court, for example. The person leading the activity session will need to ensure that the facility or location is appropriate for the planned sport and of a sufficient size to accommodate the number of participants. They will also need to make sure the facility or location is available for the date and times required.

Usually some form of booking system is available to check availability and book the facility. There is usually a cost for hiring a facility. Some locations may be free to use, such as local authority public parks, but a sports leader would need to check all of this as part of the planning process for the sports activity session.

Equipment

Most sports require some form of equipment, such as balls, rackets, nets, etc. Equipment is also required to score points, for example goals, basketball hoop, etc. In addition, other equipment may be required such as bibs. They may not be part of the usual equipment but are needed if the session is going to have some teams playing against each other; the bibs are used to show who is on which team. Cones may also be required to mark out areas of space for drills or matches.

When setting up a sports session it is important to keep track of how many pieces of each type of equipment are used. The sports leader should count them all back in when the session has come to an end to help ensure no equipment is lost.

■ It is important that a sports leader keeps track of the various sports equipment used in an activity.

Clothing

For most sports and physical activity, it is necessary to wear appropriate sports clothing. This allows the person to move freely and not be restricted by their clothing, such as if they were wearing jeans. It is also necessary to wear appropriate footwear with the right grip or cushioning.

Younger participants may often leave behind pieces of clothing after an activity session, such as sweatshirts that they have removed during the session. It is a good idea as a sports leader to check for this towards the end of the session and remind participants to take their items home with them, to help ensure they do not lose items of clothing.

For certain sports, protective clothing and equipment is required to help to keep participants safe – this has been explored in previous components. It is important that a sports leader is fully up to date with any protective clothing or equipment that is available for the sport that they are leading, so they can check participants are wearing these to help to keep them safe.

ACTIVITY

For the following sports, list the clothing and footwear (where appropriate) that is required to participate safely:

1 rugby
2 100-metre sprinting
3 swimming
4 squash.

CHECK MY LEARNING

Make a list of the equipment that you would need and an appropriate facility or location for the following sports and physical activities:

1 rounders
2 bootcamp circuits session
3 badminton.

Session plan: first part of session planning (2)

Health and safety issues

Sport and activity sessions do carry some **risks**, as these sessions will involve physical activity and in many cases different types of equipment. It is therefore important that health and safety issues are taken into account and planned for:

- during the planning stages of the session
- while leading a sport and activity session
- after the session to review the safety of the session.

Risk assessment

The most widely used and useful tool for identifying and reducing risks and hazards is a **risk assessment**. A risk assessment is something that allows leaders to identify risks and **hazards** and then make an informed choice on either how to control these risks or hazards, or avoid them altogether.

When conducting a risk assessment the process to use is as follows:

Begin by making a list of all the possible hazards that could exist for the sports activity session. Write them all down, no matter how remote you think the chances might be.

Consider the likelihood that a hazard will cause an injury.

- **Low** likelihood – unlikely to happen as long as sensible steps are taken.
- **Medium** likelihood – reasonable chance that it might happen.
- **High** likelihood – very likely to happen.

Consider the severity of the injury should the hazard cause harm.

- **Low** severity – short-term injury such as cuts, scrapes and bruises that will have little effect on performance.
- **Medium** severity – significant injury such as breaks, strains and sprains or concussion that would halt an activity and need serious medical attention.
- **High** severity – severe or potentially fatal injury.

Once the likelihood and severity have been thought about, the overall risk can be calculated using a table like Table 3.3.

KEY TERMS

Risk is an injury or harm that could happen to a person in response to a hazard.

Risk assessment is a list of possible hazards and risks associated with each hazard which shows the likelihood of them happening, and methods to reduce the risk.

Hazard is something that has the potential to cause injury.

◻ Table 3.3: Overall risk rating

Severity	Likelihood		
	Low	Medium	High
Low	Very low risk	Low risk	Medium risk
Medium	Low risk	Medium risk	High risk
High	Medium risk	High risk	Very high risk

Methods to reduce risks and hazards

You can use methods to reduce the likelihood or severity of identified hazards and risks. These methods are called control methods which act to control the chance of a person getting injured by an identified risk. This could involve using protective equipment, such as safety helmets in kayaking or pads in cricket, and safety equipment, such as ropes in rock climbing. Another term for control methods is control measures.

◻ Using protective equipment to reduce risk is called a control method.

Alternatively, you can plan to keep participants away from the identified hazards or prevent access to the hazard. You might even decide to choose a new, less risky activity if there are insufficient or inappropriate methods available to reduce the risk.

This information should then all be put into a risk assessment form.

Hazard	Risk	Likelihood of risk	Severity	Risk rating	Methods to reduce risk	Risk rating after methods to reduce risk are in place
Wet changing room floor	Slipping on changing room floor	Low	Medium	Low	Brief participants to be careful Ensure matting is in place to improve traction	Very low
Shallow water	Injuries from entering shallow end of pool	Low	High	Medium	Signs saying no diving or jumping Lifeguard on duty Under 16s must be supervised by an adult	Low
Sharp edges around pool	Cuts and scrapes from sharp edges	Low	Medium	Low	Daily checks of tiles around pool and ladders	Very low

ACTIVITY

Large numbers of people take part in the following sports every weekend:

1 football

2 mountain biking

3 cricket

4 golf

5 dinghy sailing.

Think about the environment where these activities take place and who might participate. Are there any which immediately strike you as being more risky? Place the five activities in order of which you consider to hold most risk. Provide justification of where you have placed each activity.

CHECK MY LEARNING

Complete the risk assessment template shown in Table 3.4 for a sport or activity of your choice.

☐ Table 3.4: Risk assessment template

Hazard	Risk	Likelihood of risk	Severity	Risk rating	Methods to reduce risk	Risk rating after methods to reduce risk are in place

Session plan: first part of session planning (3)

GETTING STARTED

With a partner, think about sports and activity sessions that you have taken part in outside of school. Consider if there was any paperwork you or a parent or guardian had to sign before you could take part in the activity. Discuss what sorts of things were in the paperwork and why you think this was necessary.

When a person is going to take part in sport or activity they need to know what they are going to be expected to do. This is so they can make an informed decision as to whether it is something they feel able to and want to do. This process is called informed consent.

Informed consent

An informed consent form makes the person aware of what is involved in the exercises and any risks there may be. Once the person is fully aware of what is involved, they can then give their agreement or consent to undertake the exercises, aware of any risks to health which may be involved.

The informed consent forms should inform the person:

- what is required of them
- that they can ask any questions relating to the process
- that they can stop the process at any time.

The informed consent form should be signed and dated by the participant and the person carrying out the health screening process. If the participant is under 18, a parent or guardian will also be required to give their consent to their participation in the health screening process.

Sports participation consent form (Under 18)

(Please complete in Block Capitals)

Activity/Event and date _____

Name _____

Address _____

Name and address of next of kin: Name and contact address of doctor:

_____   _____

_____   _____

_____   _____

Telephone _____   Telephone _____

Any special educational needs, disabilities, treatment, regular medication or allergies to declare (e.g. asthma, hay fever, diabetes, etc.)

_____

Special dietary requirements? _____

_____

I acknowledge receipt of and understand the details of all of the information about the activity/event and consent to the participation of:

I will make sure that my son/daughter understands the information given about his/her safety and the safety of the group, and that any rules and instructions given by staff are adhered to.

I will inform the leader of any changes to my son's/daughter's health or fitness before the start of the activity.

I am in agreement that those in charge may give permission for the participant mentioned above to receive medical/dental treatment in an emergency.

Signed (parent/guardian): _____ Date _____

Give relationship to participant if not parent:

I understand that for my own safety, and the safety of the group, I will undertake to obey the rules and instructions of members of staff.

Signed (Under 18): _____ Date _____

◨ **Figure 3.5: Informed consent form**

Explain why you think a parent or guardian needs to give their consent for a person under 18 years of age to take part in health screening processes.

Physical activity readiness questionnaire (PAR-Q)

For participants over the age of 18, a physical activity readiness questionnaire (PAR-Q) can be completed before taking part in exercise (see Figure 2.13, page 100). A PAR-Q looks at an individual's medical history and highlights any factors that could stop them from participating.

The questionnaire asks specific questions related to a person's health to try and identify if they have any incidences of heart-related problems, lung conditions such as asthma, or long-term injuries that may affect their ability to take part in sport or physical activity.

When providing someone with a questionnaire, it is important to encourage them to answer truthfully and be as accurate as possible.

An informed consent form should also be completed to confirm the person taking part in the sport or physical activity is aware of the risks of participation and agrees to them.

There is a law called the General Data Protection Regulation (GDPR) that came into place in May 2018, that means that any data taken from participants must be kept confidential and stored and accessed in line with GDPR requirements.

Discuss in small groups how you would respond if a person answered yes to any of the questions included in a PAR-Q.

Explain why a person should complete an informed consent form before taking part in a sport or activity session.

Session plan: components'

Components of session planning

Each part of the activity session is split into different components: the warm-up; the main activity; and the cool down. See Table 3.5 for an example of what a session plan may look like.

◘ **Table 3.5: One example of a session plan – key information about participants; warm-up; main activity; cool down**

Key information about participants

About the participants			
Age range:	10–11 years old	Number taking part: 12	
Are there any participants with special educational needs and disabilities (SEND)? (If yes please give details.)		None	
Ability of the participants		Beginners	
Males	6	Females	6
Sport		Basketball	

About the session					
Date:	June	Start time:	10.30 a.m.	End time:	11.15 a.m.
Resources:	12 basketballs whistle bibs stopwatch cones basketball hoops				

Session aims
Aim: Introduce travel and passing techniques in basketball **Expected outcomes:** teach participants how to dribble the ball teach participants how to pass the ball using the chest pass

Warm-up

Warm-up			
Time	Activities/practice	Organisation	Teaching points
5 mins	**Pulse raiser** Jogging in a circle Side steps facing inwards and outwards Jogging backwards Jog forwards and change direction on the whistle Touch the ground with right hand then the left on the blow of the whistle Sprint the length of the sports hall, jog the widths **Mobiliser** Hip circles Ankle circles Wrist circles **Stretch** Standing calf stretch Standing hamstring stretch Standing quadriceps stretch Standing upper back stretch	All participants move in a circle in a clockwise direction Sports leader jogs in counter clockwise direction to the participants Participants in a circle, leader in the centre of the circle	Heel toe action when jogging Look behind you when jogging backwards Bend your knees to get to touch your hand to the ground Feet pointing forwards, push your back heel into the ground Keep your chest lifted and legs straight Keep your knees together Pretend you are holding a big beach ball and stretch your shoulder blades out

The main activity

Main activity			
Time	Activities/practice	Organisation	Teaching points
10 mins	Demonstration of how to dribble a basketball Participants have a ball each and practise dribbling the ball on the spot Participants then try to move with the ball while still bouncing it Participants work in pairs One walks while dribbling the ball to the cone, picks it up and then dribbles the ball back to their partner The ball is passed to the partner who then repeats the process Repeat four times for each participant Repeat the whole drill but encourage the participants to jog with the ball and also jog around the cone rather than picking the ball up at each end	Participants work in their own space X X Cones laid out 15 m apart	Push the ball downwards with the hand Keep the ball slightly in front of you Try to look up to see where you are going while still dribbling the ball
10 mins	Demonstration of chest pass using a participant to receive the ball Participants practise passing the ball to their partner using a chest pass Moving chest pass Participants practise dribbling with the ball then passing to their partner The partner then dribbles the ball and passes back	X X Cones laid out 2 m apart Change the distance that learners need to throw the ball depending on their ability Participants run across the sports hall passing to each other Once they get to the end, they walk back to the start	Step forward as you pass the ball Hold the ball at your chest and push your arms forward As you release the ball, your hands should point to the way you want the ball to travel Push the ball downwards Try and look where you are going Stop, hold the ball then pass to your partner
15 mins	Adapted game to practise basketball techniques covered in the activity session Demonstration of the adapted game working with three participants to help to show how the game works	2 v 2 Court laid out with cones in the middle at each end of the court Each team has to dribble and pass their ball to their partner. To score, the ball has to be placed on top of the cone at the opposite end of the court	Step into the pass Push the ball downwards when dribbling Try to look up when dribbling the ball

Cool down

Pulse lowering			
Time	Activities/practice	Organisation	Teaching points
5 mins	Participants jog around the playing area gradually decreasing their pace after each lap Bring the jog down to a march Walk around more slowly in a circle **Stretch** Lying down full body stretch Lying down hamstring stretch Standing up calf stretch Standing up quadriceps stretch	All participants move in a circle in a clockwise direction Sports leader jogs in counter clockwise direction to the participants Participants in a circle, sports leader in the centre of the circle	Heel toe action when jogging Push your hands and feet as far away from your body as possible Keep your leg straight and pull your thigh towards your chest Keep both feet pointing forwards Keep knees together

CHECK MY LEARNING

Draw a template for a session plan in line with Table 3.5. Complete the session plan for a sport or physical activity of your choice, with aims and expected outcomes.

Session plan: components of a warm-up (1)

A warm-up should always be included at the start of a sport or activity session for health and safety as well as for participants' overall enjoyment and engagement in the session. A warm-up consists of three main phases: 1) pulse raiser; 2) mobiliser; 3) stretch.

Pulse raiser

The first part of a warm-up is to increase the pulse rate. Your pulse rate is also known as your heart rate. As you increase your pulse blood is pumped around your body at a faster rate. Your breathing rate will also increase in order to get more oxygen into the body which is transferred to the blood and taken to the muscles.

As the muscles contract they generate heat. This increases the temperature of the blood surrounding the working muscles. This warmed blood is pumped around the body and has the effect of helping to increase the temperature of the body and the muscles. As your muscles become warmer they become more pliable.

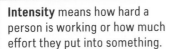

LINK IT UP

Pulse raising and the pliability of muscles is also covered in Component 1: The importance of warm-ups and cool downs before and after participation in sport and activity (pages 18–19).

Types of activities to use in a pulse raiser

The activities should gradually increase pulse rate so that the body can slowly adjust to the demands of exercise. Therefore, the types of activities should show a progressive increase in **intensity**.

KEY TERM

Intensity means how hard a person is working or how much effort they put into something.

It's a good idea to start a pulse raiser with a brisk walk, increasing the length of stride and pace. This can then be progressed to a slow jog and then include activities such as side steps and jogging backwards to add variation. Adding in arm movements also helps to increase the intensity of the activity as it places greater demand on the body.

Games can be included in the pulse raiser, such as jogging then responding to instructions from the sports leader such as touching the ground with the right and then left hand, jumping up in the air and sitting on the floor at different intervals between jogs. By the end of the pulse raiser, a participant's pulse rate should have increased, their body temperature should have increased and they should be breathing more quickly.

LINK IT UP

Intensity in the context of physical activity is covered in Component 1: Physiological, psychological and environmental causes of common sporting injuries (pages 24–25).

Mobilise

After taking part in pulse raising activities, it is necessary to mobilise the joints of the body ready for participation in physical activity. The joints in the body that allow movement to take place contain a lubricant called synovial fluid. This helps the bones that meet at the joint to slide over each other more easily. During the warm-up phase of an activity session, more synovial fluid is released into the joint which increases the ability of the joints to move more freely. The mobilise section in particular helps with this process as it gets the joints to move through their full range of movement which has the effect of increasing the release of synovial fluid.

Main joints of the body

The main joints that need to be mobilised in the body include:

- shoulders
- wrists
- hips
- knees
- ankles.

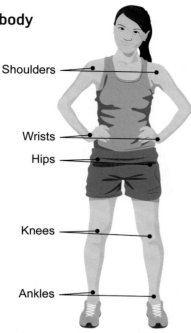

Shoulders
Wrists
Hips
Knees
Ankles

◻ Figure 3.6: The main joints of the body that should be mobilised in a warm-up

Types of activities to use in a mobiliser section of a warm-up

Activities to mobilise the joints should start with small movements and gradually work up to larger movements as the joints warm up and get used to the movements being carried out.

- Neck – turning the head to both sides and placing the chin on the chest.
- Shoulders – with bent elbows, circle the shoulders backwards and then forwards, then straighten the arms, circling arms forwards and backwards.
- Elbows – bend and straighten arms.
- Wrists – bend and straighten wrists and circle the hands in one direction and then back in the other direction.
- Back – side bends.
- Pelvis – hip circles, moving the pelvis round in one direction and then back in the other direction.
- Knees – knee raises, squats and lunges.
- Ankles – toe taps, circling the foot in one direction and then back in the other direction.

ACTIVITY

Describe different activities from those listed that can be used in the mobiliser section of a warm-up.

CHECK MY LEARNING

For a sport or activity of your choice, describe suitable pulse raising and mobilising activities. Consider which joints are going to be used when taking part in that sport. Make a list of the main joints that should be mobilised in a warm-up with activities that could be carried out to mobilise these joints.

Session plan: components of a warm-up (2)

The last part of a warm-up is to stretch the muscles that are going to be used in the main activity. This is often called the prep-stretch.

Stretching

Stretching the muscles that are going to be used in the main activity helps to fully prepare them for exercise and prevent injury from muscle strains. A muscle strain is when the muscle stretches too far and some of the muscle fibres tear.

Location of the main muscles of the body

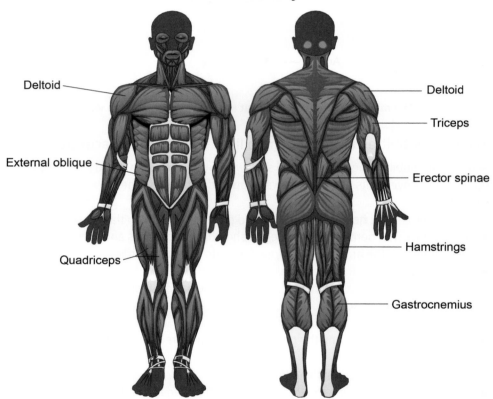

Deltoid

External oblique

Quadriceps

Deltoid

Triceps

Erector spinae

Hamstrings

Gastrocnemius

◻ Figure 3.7: The main muscles of the body

ACTIVITY

Write down each of the main muscles on sticky notes. Place each note on a partner over the correct location for each muscle group. Use the diagram to check your placement of each note.

Types of stretches

There are two main types of stretches used in a warm-up:

- static – where a person holds a position to stretch a muscle for a short period of time
- dynamic – these are carried out through active movements of the muscle which still stretch the muscle but the position is not held.

Static stretching

The following positions can be used to stretch the main muscle groups shown in Figure 3.7.

Deltoids   Triceps   Erector spinae   Obliques

Quadriceps   Hamstrings   Gastrocnemius

□ **Figure 3.8: Static stretching positions to stretch the main muscle groups**

CHECK MY LEARNING

Draw stick diagrams of a person to show the different positions to stretch the following muscles:

deltoids	quadriceps
triceps	hamstrings
erector spinae	gastrocnemius.
obliques	

Session plan: the main component (1)

Once a warm-up has been carried out, participants should be ready to take part in the main component of a sports activity session.

Activities in the main component

The main component of a sports activity session will take up most of the sports session. This could consist of one main activity, such as a circuit training session, or it could be broken down into a skills session followed by a game; for example 20 minutes spent practising a sports skill such as passing and 20 minutes spent playing a game and using the skill in the game situation. The physical activities within the main component of an activity session might involve running, or walking, or comprise an exercise class.

There are a variety of types of activities that can be included in the main component, such as:
- fitness for playing sport
- fitness through fun
- fitness through interactive activities
- sport-specific drills and adapted games.

The length of the main component of a sports activity session will determine how many types of activities are included in the session. The main aims of the sports activity session will also decide what activities would be most appropriate to include in the main component.

Type

Some activity sessions are aimed at increasing physical fitness. In these sessions, specific components of fitness will be targeted for development. For example:
- a circuit training fitness session may be designed to develop aerobic endurance. In this session, each of the exercise stations would involve aerobic endurance-based activities such as skipping, shuttle runs, step-ups, etc., which all increase the heart rate and breathing rate and therefore challenge the cardiorespiratory system
- a participant may want to improve their skills for a specific sport, e.g. participants in a rugby team may take part in training sessions to develop their passing and tackling skills to help to improve their performance in a game
- participants may take part in training to train specific components of fitness, to help to improve their performance in a particular sport, e.g. a rugby player may go to the gym and carry out resistance training to improve their strength to help them perform well in a scrum.

Some activity sessions are designed to be fun; these are often aimed at children to help them to see sport and physical activity as a fun thing to do and encourage them to continue to participate as they grow up. Adults may also want to take part in an activity session because they find it fun, such as a Zumba session.

Some activity sessions include interactive activities to help to improve fitness and add new dynamics to a session, such as competition against other participants. For instance, spinning classes can have interactive technology that allows racing to take place in the class against other spinners.

◪ Some sessions may provide fitness through a fun activity like Zumba.

Sport-specific drills

If one of the main aims of a sports activity session is to improve performance in a specific sport, the main component will usually include **sport-specific drills**. These are used to practise and develop skills and techniques that are used in a specific sport. The sports leader will plan a variety of drills that gradually increase in demand for that specific skill, moving from practising the skill in unopposed situations to pressurised drills using active opposition.

KEY TERM

Sport-specific drills are exercises used to develop sporting techniques used in specific sports.

ACTIVITY

Write down three different drills that could be used in a sport of your choice to practise drills with opposition.

Adapted games

An adapted game is where the participants take part in a competitive game but the rules are changed to ensure specific techniques can be developed in a game situation.

After a sports leader has led a range of sport-specific drills it is a good idea to include an adapted game in the main component of a sports activity session. This is so that the techniques practised in the drills can be tested and put into a competitive situation.

An adapted game can be used whereby the team are only permitted to use the specified technique during the game. For example, if the drills are focused on developing dribbling, the adapted game could require all players in a team to dribble the ball before that team can score.

CHECK MY LEARNING

1 Explain why drill practice is used in a sports activity session.
2 Describe how drills can be progressed in a sports activity session to help to prepare participants for a competitive game.

Session plan: the main component (2)

GETTING STARTED

Make a list of all the sports you know that require some form of passing technique in order to play the sport.

◻ In a passing drill, pairs of players can gradually increase the space between them as their technique improves.

Passing drills

Passing is the process of giving an object to another person in the same team. In sport, the object is often a ball; however, not all sports use balls, for example ice hockey uses a puck.

Each sport requires different techniques to perform a pass, although the principles of improving passing technique remain fairly similar. First of all, unopposed practices are carried out which means participants are just passing to each other. The distance each participant stands apart from their partner can be increased as they improve their technique. This allows the participants to focus on the key requirements of the technique without having to think about or perform additional skills or techniques.

ACTIVITY

For a sport of your choice, write down two unopposed activity drills that you could use to practise a technique of your choice.

Passing: travel drills

The introduction of travel makes performing the technique a little more difficult. In some sports the participant will travel with the ball, such as basketball and football. For other sports, such as netball, a participant only travels after the ball has been passed.

Travel drills can involve participants making their way across a sports hall or pitch while passing the ball to each other in order to get to one end.

Introduction of passive opposition or active opposition can help to increase the level of difficulty of the drill.

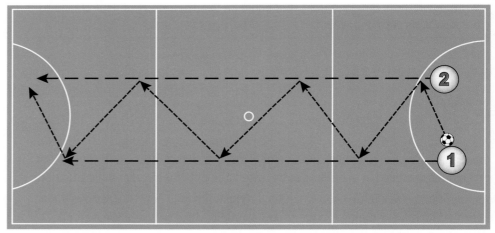

◻ Figure 3.9: Adding travelling to passing drills makes it a little more difficult

ACTIVITY

For a sport of your choice, write down how you could add travel to a drill to practise a specific technique.

Passing: pressurised drills

Pressurised drills introduce speed or more opponents to work against participants who are trying to get the ball from them. This again adds further difficulty to the drill as participants are having to travel and also now ensure they pass the ball to their team mates while having to avoid members of the opposing team.

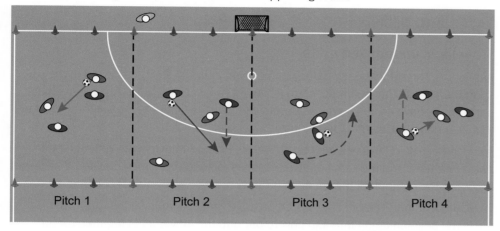

■ Figure 3.10: Pressurised drills introduce speed or more opponents to further increase difficulty

ACTIVITY

For a sport of your choice, write down how you could use a pressurised drill to practise a specific technique.

Passing: adapted game

The passing skill can then be used in an adapted game so that participants can explore how to use the skill in a game situation.

To ensure the skill of passing is practised, rules can be introduced, such as every participant has to pass the ball before the team can score, or every type of pass permitted for a specific sport has to be demonstrated before the team can score.

CHECK MY LEARNING

For a different sport from the one you used in the activities, describe drills that you would use to practise passing.

Session plan: the main component (3)

> **GETTING STARTED**
>
> For some sports, participants are permitted to travel with the ball or object that is used to score in the game. In others, travelling while holding the ball is not permitted.
>
> Make a list of all the sports you know that:
> - permit travelling with the ball or object
> - do not permit travelling with the ball or object.

Getting the ball or object past other players, and ultimately to the place where a participant can score, is a very important part of many sports.

Travelling drills

Travelling: unopposed drills

It is very important that each participant is given a ball, or the object used in the sport, to practise the technique of travelling for that specific sport. This means that participants have as much time as possible to focus on learning the technique rather than standing and waiting for their turn.

A coach once said, 'You wouldn't teach a class to learn how to write with one pen between them', and the same principle applies to sport. Every person should have access to the equipment they need in order to practise a sporting technique.

To begin, the sports leader should demonstrate the technique so that participants know the position to get into and how to perform the movements required for the technique. As the technique is travelling, there will be some travel introduced during this phase of the drill.

Examples of travelling drills

In basketball, each participant dribbles their basketball walking around the sports hall, all travelling in the same direction.

To increase the difficulty, participants can then be told they can walk around the sports hall in any direction they wish. This will mean they will have to pay more attention to where they are going as they will start to encounter other participants and need to be able to change direction to move out of their way.

To further increase the difficulty, the speed of travel can be increased from a walk to a slow jog, initially all participants going in the same direction, such as all in a line going to one side of the sports hall and back. Any direction can then be introduced to increase the difficulty.

> **ACTIVITY**
>
> For a selected sport of your choice that permits travelling with the ball, describe progressive unopposed practice drills.

Travelling: active opponent drills

To add pressure to a travel drill, opponents will need to be introduced. The opponents need to try to stop the participant with the ball from travelling any further.

This can be done with a two versus two situation. Each player has to travel with the ball until an opponent prevents them from travelling any further. They then have to pass the ball to their partner and the partner continues until they are stopped by an opponent. This is repeated until the opponents take the ball and then they continue with the drill.

ACTIVITY

For a selected sport of your choice that permits travelling with the ball, describe a pressurised drill activity.

Travelling: adapted game

To ensure all participants get to practise travelling in an adapted game, the rules can be changed so that each player has to demonstrate some travel with the ball before the team can score. Players in the team could be given a certain distance or certain number of steps that they have to take when travelling with the ball to ensure that they are demonstrating the skill. The players that are already able to travel well with the ball could be asked to travel a greater distance before passing compared with players that are still developing their travelling skills.

CHECK MY LEARNING

For a different sport that you have not covered already, describe drills that you would use to practise travelling.

You should follow the process of increasing difficulty from isolated practices to an adapted game.

Session plan: the main component (4)

In most team sports, participants can try to intercept the target object, such as a ball, in order to win it back so that their team can take possession. For a selected sport, identify ways in which players may try to intercept the target object if a ball isn't used in the sport.

Interception is when a player from an opposing team manages to get the target object when it is being passed between players on the same team. In many sports, the target object is a ball. In this section, drills that can be used to practise intercepting are explored.

Interception drills

Interception: active opposition drills

To help participants get used to the idea of interception, simple drills using three people can be used. The drill is based on the principles of a game that many people have played, which is usually called 'piggy in the middle'.

- Participants are grouped into threes.
- Two participants act as team members and need to pass the ball to each other using passing techniques that are specific to that sport.
- The third member of the group stands between the two players and has to try and get the ball as it is passed between the two.

◨ Figure 3.11: Active opposition drills can be based on the 'piggy in the middle' game

ACTIVITY

For a selected team sport of your choice, describe an active opposition drill to practise interception.

Interception: travelling practice

To increase the difficulty, travel can be introduced where the participants are having to move around an area while still trying to intercept the ball.

Small areas and three participants can be used for most sports. The participants who are passing the ball between each other are now permitted to travel with the ball (assuming the sport allows this) and then make a pass to their partner. The third participant in the group has to now mark one of the participants who is either passing the ball or having it passed to them to try and then intercept the ball when it is being thrown.

Interception: pressurised drills

To add pressure, the groups can be increased to six in a group, so it is now three versus three with two interceptors. The players on each team need to pass to each other while the other two players need to intercept the ball.

ACTIVITY

For a selected sport of your choice, describe a pressurised drill activity to practise interception.

Interception – adapted game

To ensure all participants get to practise interception in an adapted game, the rules can be changed so that the team can only score after the ball has been intercepted from the other team.

CHECK MY LEARNING

For a different sport that you have not covered already, describe drills that you would use to practise interception.

You should follow the process of increasing difficulty from isolated practices to an adapted game.

Session plan: the main component (5)

For a range of different team sports, make a list to identify all the different ways a participant can score points.

In every team sport, there is a way that the team can score points, such as scoring a try in rugby. Scoring points is vital for a team to win so it is important that time is spent learning this technique. For some sports, not all players are able to score points; for example in netball, where only the goal shooter and goal attack are able to shoot. In this section, drills that can be used to practise scoring are explored.

Scoring drills

Scoring: unopposed drill

Every participant needs to be able to practise the techniques that can be used to score points. Rugby has two different methods to score points – scoring a try and also kicking the ball over the crossbar.

Most sports, however, have only one method of scoring points, by getting the ball or puck into a target area, for example in hockey.

To learn the technique, participants can start by performing the scoring action without having to actually aim for a goal. For example in basketball, participants can be taught to throw the ball up in the air to practise the backspin which is used in shooting a basketball hoop. This can then be progressed to throwing the ball against a wall to practise the forward direction that the ball is thrown in.

ACTIVITY

For a selected team sport of your choice, describe an isolated drill activity to practise scoring.

Scoring: passive opposition drill

To increase the difficulty, travel can be introduced. Participants could stand in two lines, either side of the target area. The sports leader passes the ball to participants on one side of the target area and the participant takes the ball and tries to score. At the same time, the participant in the opposite line runs in to retrieve the ball after the person has attempted to score. They then rejoin the lines on opposite sides so they take it in turns to score and retrieve the ball. This drill helps to ensure the back of the goal or goal area is not covered with discarded balls!

The sports leader can vary the passes to each participant depending on their ability.

Scoring: active opposition drill

Having an opponent introduces pressure to a drill. Participants can be put into groups of two versus two and they have to work together to score. Each team has to try and get the ball from each other and then try to score.

ACTIVITY

For a selected sport of your choice, describe a pressurised drill activity to practise scoring.

Scoring: adapted game

To ensure all participants get to practise scoring in an adapted game, the rules can be changed so that a team member is only able to score once in the game and cannot score again until the rest of the team have scored.

CHECK MY LEARNING

For a different sport that you have not covered already, describe drills that you would use to practise scoring.

You should follow the process of increasing difficulty from isolated practices to an adapted game.

Session plan: components of a cool down

GETTING STARTED

Consider what you have done in the last 5 to 10 minutes of a sports activity session or PE lesson – are there any activities you always seem to do? Make a note of all the things you think of and compare your list with a partner.

KEY TERM

Intensity means how hard a person is working or how much effort they put into something.

At the end of a sport or activity session it is important that a cool down takes place to help to return the body to its pre-exercise state. The cool down helps the body recover from the activity session and consists of a digressive activity (to lower the pulse) and a stretch of all the main muscles used in the activity.

Pulse lowering

The first part of the cool down consists of lowering the pulse. This involves participants gradually decreasing their pulse rate and also their breathing rate so that their cardiorespiratory system can gradually return to pre-exercise levels. Therefore, the activities should show a progressive decrease in **intensity**.

It's a good idea to start pulse lowering so that it incorporates elements of the main component activity, so that the session flows. This may be going from a game of hockey to each person having a ball and running around the field dribbling the ball. Gradually the length of stride and pace will be reduced to a slow jog. The hockey balls could then all be shot into a net and the participants slowly jog around a small section of the pitch. This can then be brought down to a fast walk, eventually coming down to a slower walk.

Cool-down stretch

When a person is taking part in physical activity, the movements that a person makes are due to muscles contracting. When a muscle contracts it will usually get shorter to produce the force required to move a specific part of the body. Some muscles, such as the hamstrings and quadriceps, are used continually when a person is running which means these muscles are repeatedly contracting. Once a person stops exercising, the muscles can remain in a slightly contracted state which means they are a little shorter than before they took part in the exercise. The more exercise sessions a person takes part in, the more contracted the muscles will become and the shorter the muscles will get. This will eventually result in a decrease in that person's flexibility and an increased risk of straining a muscle.

To help to reduce this shortening of muscles, the cool-down stretch is used to return the working muscles back to their resting length. It can also be used to increase the length of a participant's muscles if increased flexibility is of benefit to the participant.

After taking part in sport and physical activity, the increased pliability of the muscles will also be evident as many people can perform stretches to a much greater degree, and this can be seen in the cool-down part of an activity session.

Types of stretches to use in the cool-down stretch

The main muscles that have been used in the main component of the sports activity session should be stretched in the cool down. These muscles can be stretched using either maintenance stretches or developmental stretches.

Maintenance stretches

For some muscle groups a maintenance stretch can be used. A maintenance stretch is held for 15 seconds and is used to maintain the length of the muscle, as increased flexibility in that muscle is not usually beneficial to sporting performance.

As this type of stretch is only held for a short period of time, standing positions are often used, which can be the same ones used in the prep-stretch carried out during the warm-up. You will find stretches for the deltoids, triceps, gastrocnemius, quadriceps and obliques in the warm-up section.

Developmental stretches

These are held for longer, usually around 30 seconds, to help to lengthen the muscle. As these stretches are held for some time, lying down positions are often used. This can be more comfortable for participants and also help them to focus on stretching the muscle itself.

■ Figure 3.12: Developmental stretches, such as this hip flexor stretch, help to lengthen muscles

■ Figure 3.13: Some developmental stretches are best performed lying down as they are held for longer

---

ACTIVITY

Draw diagrams to show appropriate positions that could be used to stretch each of the muscle groups requiring a developmental stretch after an activity session.

CHECK MY LEARNING

1 Explain why a cool-down stretch should be used after an activity session.

2 Identify the main muscle groups that should be stretched after a sport of your choice.

3 Identify if the stretch for each muscle group should be a maintenance stretch or developmental stretch.

Learning aim B: assessment practice

How you will be assessed

For this part of the component you will need to demonstrate your ability to plan a sport or activity session for a specific target group. The plan should include the FITT principles and principles of training that were covered in Component 2.

CHECKPOINT

Strengthen

- Create a session plan for a sport or activity of your choice for a specific target group.
- Provide a detailed breakdown of each of the components in the session including warm-up, main component and cool down, giving reasons for the choice of activities used in each section.
- Ensure the plan takes into account ways to engage the target group for the given aim of the session.
- Produce a risk assessment for the planned session which includes control measures to overcome any issues identified.
- Assess how physical and psychological benefits can be gained for the participants who are taking part in the planned session.

Challenge

- Explain how technology can be used in the session.
- Assess how health monitoring information can be used to help determine the aim of the session.

ASSESSMENT ACTIVITY	LEARNING AIM	B

1 Using the template below, write a session plan for a target audience from the following types of groups:

- children and young people
- people with disabilities
- older people
- people from particular ethnic groups
- women
- LGBTI.

About the participants: Target group		
Age range:		
Are there any participants with special educational needs and disabilities (SEND)? (If yes please give details.)		
Ability of the participants		
Sport or activity		
About the session		

Date		Start time		End time	11.00 a.m.
Resources					

Session aim	

Component			
Time	Activities/practice	Organisation	Teaching points

Complete a risk assessment for the planned activity and provide any control measures where required.

2 Provide justification as to why the activities have been chosen for the specific target group.

TAKE IT FURTHER

Provide evidence of how health monitoring has been taken into account to help to determine the aim of the session for the target group.

Explore different types of technology that could be used to help to improve the enjoyment of the session for the participants.

Methods of delivery/success (1)

GETTING STARTED

Make a list of the types of drill that can be used to practise a sporting technique, with descriptions of what each type of drill involves.

The sports leader should confirm with the participants at the start of the session what their ability levels are. This is so that the sports leader can be sure the planned session will be appropriate for the group. If the sports leader finds out at the start of the session that the participants are not of the ability that they had expected, the leader will know that they need to adapt the planned activities. Once the participants have arrived, it is the sports leader's responsibility to prepare them for the sports activity session.

Practical application of the main content of the planned session

The main content of a sports activity session is usually the main component as this will take up most of the sports session. This section of a sports activity session usually includes drills to practise a specific sporting technique, an adapted game and a full game.

The aims of the session will determine what activities are included in the main component. However, the main component will usually contain some of the sections outlined below.

Skill introduction – whatever the main aims of the session are, this element is designed to introduce the skill. It may involve a simple drill where the basic technique is practised; see Table 3.6.

◘ **Table 3.6: Introduction of a simple drill where the basic technique is practised**

Main component		
Activities/practice	**Organisation**	**Teaching points**
Demonstration of how to dribble a basketball	Participants work in their own space	Push the ball downwards with the hand
Participants have a ball each and practise dribbling the ball on the spot		
Participants then try to move with the ball while still bouncing it	X X Cones laid out 15 m apart	Keep the ball slightly in front of you
Participants work in pairs One walks while dribbling the ball to the cone, picks it up and then dribbles the ball back to their partner The ball is passed to the partner who then repeats the process Repeat four times for each participant Repeat the whole drill but encourage the participants to jog with the ball and also jog around the cone rather than picking the ball up at each end		Try to look up to see where you are going while still dribbling the ball

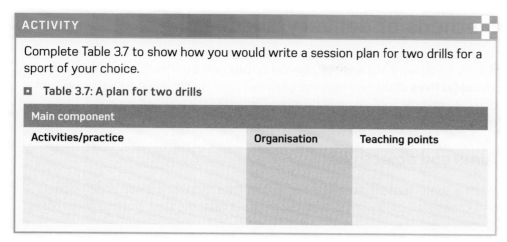

Complete Table 3.7 to show how you would write a session plan for two drills for a sport of your choice.

◻ Table 3.7: A plan for two drills

Main component		
Activities/practice	Organisation	Teaching points

Development – as the session progresses, the drills should become more challenging in order to make the practice more game-specific. The development of these skills is called 'progression'. Progressions are achieved by bringing in more complex situations, for example passing a moving ball or passing to keep the ball away from an opponent.

Adapted game – an adapted or conditioned game is designed to reinforce the elements that were practised in the drills. This type of game will have certain rules that help the participants put into practice the skills they have developed in the session so far.

◻ Table 3.8: An example of an adapted game in a session plan

Time	Activities/practice	Organisation	Teaching points
10 mins	Adapted game to practise basketball techniques covered in the activity session Demonstration of the adapted game working with three participants to help to show how the game works	2 v 2 Court laid out with cones at each end of the court Each team has to dribble and pass their ball to their partner. To score, the ball has to be placed on top of the cone at the opposite end of the court	Step into the pass Push the ball downwards when dribbling Try to look up when dribbling the ball

Devise an adapted game to practise the techniques covered in the previous activity for your selected sport. Complete Table 3.9 to show how you would write a session plan for this adapted game.

◻ Table 3.9: A plan for an adapted game

Main component		
Activities/practice	Organisation	Teaching points

Full game – most sports activity sessions will finish the main component with a full game to practise other techniques and tactics in a game situation.

Methods of delivery/success (2)

 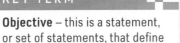
Successful delivery of a sport or physical activity session should mean that the aims and **objectives** of the session have been met. One way to achieve this is to ensure that the practical application of the main content of the planned session is carried out as intended.

Aims and objectives

When a sports leader has selected an appropriate sport for a group of participants and knows their ability range, they can work out what the aims and objectives of the session should be.

An aim is a statement of intent, usually written in broad terms, which sets out what the sports leader hopes to achieve by the end of the activity session, or set of sessions. An objective is a statement, or set of statements, that define measurable outcomes, i.e. the steps taken to achieve the desired outcome (aim). In order to assist with the planning of activity sessions, sports leaders should be very clear about the aim(s) of their sessions and the objectives (steps) they will need to take to achieve their aim(s).

It is important that the aims and objectives are realistic for each group of participants so that each participant has the ability to achieve them.

So that everyone is fully aware of what the activity session is going to be focused on, the sports leader should run through the aims and objectives of the session at the start. This provides the participants with an idea of the sorts of things they will be doing in that session and helps to prepare them mentally for the session.

ACTIVITY

Practise writing aims and objectives for three different sports or activity sessions, ensuring they meet the definition of what an aim and an objective is.

Organisation of a sports activity session

When leading a sport or physical activity session, the person leading the activity must be able to apply their organisational skills to help ensure the session runs smoothly and meets the set aims and objectives of the session.

Organisation before the session starts

There are some checks that should be carried out by the sports leader before the participants arrive. It is therefore important for a sports leader to arrive early for their session so that they are able to complete these pre-sports activity session preparations.

- A sports leader should collect their equipment prior to the session.
- The equipment will need to be checked and dealt with, such as putting goals up or pumping up balls, so that as soon as the participants arrive they are able to get started rather than wait for the sports leader to get everything ready.
- If equipment is damaged it shouldn't be used. Therefore the sports leader will need to give themselves time to find alternative equipment for the session if they find equipment is damaged.

ACTIVITY

Make notes on how you would introduce a sports activity session for a sport of your choice and at a facility of your choice. Once you have written the introduction down, practise saying it out loud a few times so that you can get used to the process of introducing a sports activity session.

Organisation when using a session plan

As a sports leader you may be asked to plan a session and in so doing write a session plan. Part of the role may also require you to interpret a session plan that is written by another sports leader. As such, you will need to know what each part of a session plan should contain and what it means.

The first parts of a session plan are quite straightforward in relation to the information about the participants. The section that lists the activities and organisation of the activities should be written clearly so that any person using the session plan is clear on how the activity should be set out and what the participants should be doing.

Organisation after the session has finished

Any equipment used will need to be checked to ensure it is not damaged and still in good working order before being stored away. Some sports leaders will enlist the help of participants with this part of the session. This can help develop children's confidence as they may feel this is a position of responsibility and respond well to this request for help. The equipment then needs to be placed in its appropriate area.

Once the equipment has been checked and properly stored away, the sports leader should carry out an inspection of the facility to ensure it is in a fit state for the next people to use. This may involve picking up any dropped litter or mopping up any liquids from the floor from spilt drinks or perspiration.

CHECK MY LEARNING

Create a checklist of the activities a leader should complete pre-session and post-session, with descriptions of what each activity involves and why it should be carried out.

Methods of delivery/success (3)

GETTING STARTED

One of the main priorities of any sports leader is maintaining safety. Imagine that you have been asked to take a group of five participants out for a 3 km run from your school and back. Consider what health and safety checks you should carry out before, during and after the run.

LINK IT UP

To see an example of a PAR-Q, see Component 2: Understanding fitness programmes (page 100).

It is important that a sport and activity session is delivered safely and that a sports leader's appearance is appropriate for delivering a physical activity session.

Health and safety checks

Health and safety checks should be carried out before, during and after a sport or physical activity session.

Participants

It is important for a sports leader to check the participants are fit to take part in the sport or activity session and identify any previous injuries that may affect participation. This can be carried out using a PAR-Q.

This should also be followed up with a verbal check prior to participation to find out whether the participants have any recent injuries that were not previously declared on the PAR-Q. This will help the sports leader to identify if any activities are not appropriate for the participant and provide alternatives that are appropriate, without the risk of further injury to the affected area.

Identification of hazards prior to a sport or activity session

A risk assessment should be completed prior to the session and any hazards identified. Methods to reduce the identified risks should then be put in place. For example, in a sports hall, football 5-A-Side goals would be classed as a hazard if they are not going to be used, for instance if the planned activity session was to be gymnastics. This is because if they are set up, a person may be at risk of bumping into them or getting caught in the netting and tripping over. Therefore, the control measure would be to put the 5-A-Side goal away into an appropriate storage facility.

Control measures can be put into place if the identified hazard cannot be removed. In this situation, if the 5-A-Side goals could not be removed then benches could be placed around them to prevent participants from going near them.

ACTIVITY

Visit a sports hall or sporting area. Check the area for potential hazards, noting any risks they may cause. For each hazard identified, describe methods that could be used to reduce these risks, or control measures.

Identification of hazards during a sport or activity session

At the start of each sports activity session, it is important that a sports leader runs through the emergency procedures of the sports facility that they are in. This is to help to protect both the participants and the sports leader so that everyone is aware of what they should do in an emergency situation. The sports leader should cover the following:

- location of fire exits
- location of first aid box
- where the nearest first aider is located in the building
- location of a phone or method of communication that can be used to summon help in case of an emergency.

The sports leader should ensure participants know the answer to all of these in advance of the session. This may require talking to the facilities duty manager if they are at a new site.

ACTIVITY

In a sports facility of your choice, find out the emergency procedures so that you would know what to do if you were working as a sports leader at that facility.

Health and safety will continue to be a concern for a person leading a sport or physical activity session while the session is taking place. The person leading the session must be ready to spot potential hazards and implement methods to reduce the risks, or put in place control measures to minimise the risk of the identified hazard. For example, a simple check is to alert participants if you see that their laces are untied, asking them to stop and tie their laces before continuing, to help to prevent them from tripping over.

In throwing events such as the shot put, during practice the participants all need to be in a line a safe distance apart from each other. They should also know that they can only retrieve their shot put when all participants have finished throwing. This is to prevent anyone from being hit when retrieving their shot put.

ACTIVITY

Explain how you would respond to the following hazards during a sports activity session to maintain the health and safety of participants, giving reasons for your actions.

1 Spilt water on the floor in a sports hall during a basketball session
2 Several participants losing control of their hockey balls in a hockey passing drill and hockey balls going into other participants' playing area
3 A springboard breaking during a gymnastics session.

Identification of hazards after a sport or physical activity session

Once the sport or physical activity session has finished and participants have left, the person leading the activity session should ensure they leave the facility in the way they found it. Any litter should be removed, as this could be a potential tripping or slipping hazard for participants in the next sport or physical activity session. Any broken or faulty equipment should be reported and removed to prevent others from potentially getting injured if they were to use it.

Appearance

The personal appearance of a sports leader is very important. Sports leaders must remember that they are setting the standard to the participants that they lead. By dressing in the appropriate clothing, footwear and having the right equipment, the sports leader looks the part which helps to show the participants who the leader is. Appropriate presentation by the sports leader will demonstrate what the sports leader expects each participant to wear in order to take part in the sports session. This can also help a sports leader to feel more confident when leading a session. It is important to note that good standards of personal hygiene are expected for a sports leader to prevent body odour.

◘ Sports leaders should wear appropriate clothing and footwear, and have the correct equipment.

CHECK MY LEARNING ■■

1 For a sport or physical activity session of your choice, explain the key hazards you should look out for before and during an activity session, the methods you would use to reduce the risk, and any control measures you would put in place.

2 For a sport of your choice, make a list of the correct clothing, footwear and equipment a sports leader should have in order to be presented appropriately.

Methods of delivery/success (4)

In order to meet the set aims and objectives of the session, it is important that the person leading the session is able to follow the session plan effectively but also take into account the ability of the participants. An effective sports leader is able to adapt the session to meet participants' needs.

Adapting the session to participants' needs

To adapt a session, the sports leader needs to be able to assess how each participant is performing and know how to make the drills, exercises or adapted game more difficult to provide the right level of challenge. Alternatively, they may need to make it easier so that a participant is able to perform the set task. It may be necessary to adapt certain activities to take into account the ability and fitness level of each participant, otherwise the activity could result in the person getting injured if they are not able to perform the technique correctly, or are too tired to be able to perform the activity safely.

Teaching points should be given to help the participants know what they need to do and how the activity or exercise can be adapted. The teaching points should be short and precise so that participants are able to remember what the sports leader has said and apply this when they are practising the technique.

For example, when a participant is not able to perform a full press-up, teaching points could include:

- bend your knees so that you are kneeling on the floor
- keep your back straight
- bend your arms at the elbows.

◾ Figure 3.14: Press-ups can be adapted to suit ability

The sports leader should then reinforce these teaching points while observing participants carrying out the activity, with positive reinforcement such as 'Great, your back is nice and straight'.

It is not usually a good idea to tell participants what not to do when adapting a sporting technique or exercise. This is because some participants may not hear correctly and actually think the sports leader is telling them what they should be doing. For example, rather than saying to participants, 'Don't look down', a sports leader should say 'Keep your head up and look forwards'.

Use of equipment and technology

Equipment and technology can be used in sport and activity sessions for a variety of purposes.

- To monitor the intensity that participants are working at to ensure they are putting in sufficient effort, as well as meeting a specific training intensity which will lead to fitness gains. To do this, smartwatches, activity trackers and heart rate monitors can be worn by participants.
- To add variety to the sport or activity session. For example, introducing new equipment can help to motivate participants as they learn how to use it, such as adding in speed, agility and quickness equipment like low hurdles or ladders . It can also add an element of fun and novelty to a session.
- To improve participant performance. For example, audio-visual footage of a participant performing a specific technique can be taken and reviewed using performer analysis software to help to show areas for development with their sporting technique.

CHECK MY LEARNING

1 For a sports drill or activity of your choice, explain how you would adapt it:
  - to increase the level of demand
  - to decrease the level of demand
  - for participants of different ages and different abilities.

2 Explain how three different types of equipment and technology can be used in the following sessions:
  - tennis
  - group workout exercise class
  - long-distance running.

ACTIVITY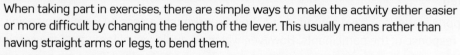

When taking part in exercises, there are simple ways to make the activity either easier or more difficult by changing the length of the lever. This usually means rather than having straight arms or legs, to bend them.

Lower weights can be used if the exercise uses weights, or bodyweight could be used as an alternative if lighter than the weights provided in a session.

High impact exercises that involve having both feet off the floor at any one time, as in running and jumping, can be made easier by converting these to low impact, where there is always one foot on the ground.

For the following exercises, provide adaptations that make them:

a) easier

b) more difficult.
  - Sit-ups
  - Tricep dips
  - Jumping jacks

Methods of reviewing (1)

All good sports leaders will continually review each sports activity session that they have planned and led. This allows them to explore areas that they feel are working well and areas that they need to develop to help them to become a more effective sports leader.

Reviewing own progress in sports leadership skills

Throughout a career, it is always a good idea for every individual to take some time to reflect on how they are doing. This reflection is actually a form of review which presents the individual with clear evidence of how they are developing their skills and succeeding in specific aspects of the role, which can be a highly effective motivator.

During this reflection and review period, however, areas for development should also be focused on. There is always something we can do to improve and develop – even for the very experienced and most successful sports leaders.

Methods of reviewing

Once the sports activity session has finished, it is good practice to allow a few minutes for a formal conclusion to complete the session as well as carry out activities that will help sports leaders to review the session.

Questionnaires

Some participants would rather not provide feedback directly to a sports leader, especially if it is negative. Therefore, one method of gaining feedback is to give participants a questionnaire at the end. The questionnaire should be as brief as possible.

Video

A sports leader can have a good idea of how they thought a session went from seeing the response of the participants. However, watching audio-visual footage of the session will give a much more accurate representation. The sports leader will see many aspects of their sports leadership skills, such as how they communicate with the participants and if there are any parts of the communication that were not clear. They can observe their own practical demonstrations and listen to the coaching points given as well as how they organised the participants. It takes time to set up audio-visual equipment but the information it gives a sports leader on how they have performed is very valuable.

Comment cards

These can be very brief and allow participants to write an overall comment on what they thought about the session – they may highlight something they particularly enjoyed or something that they weren't happy with. More participants are likely to complete one of these compared to a longer questionnaire.

Direct verbal feedback

Sports leaders should ask for direct verbal feedback at various points during the session as well as at the end, e.g. 'Do you all understand?', 'How are you finding this activity?' etc. Use open questions such as 'In what ways did you enjoy the activity session?' followed by 'Which parts did you like best?' to gain a better understanding of their thoughts. You should also ask if there were any parts that participants didn't enjoy, followed by questions to find out why not.

Feedback from participants

It is always good practice to allow the participants a chance to feed back to the sports leader on what they thought of the session, including what they have or haven't enjoyed. While the sports leader may have thought the session went really well, the participants may not have enjoyed certain aspects but perhaps were too polite or shy to show this. This feedback helps the sports leader to understand the needs of each participant and inform their planning of the next sports activity session, and helps to cater for individual needs as well as group needs.

Feedback from supervisor

A supervisor will be able to provide clear informed feedback about the sports session and the leadership skills, qualities and conduct that they witnessed. They will know what to expect and what is good practice so can clearly feed back about the key areas that went well, plus any areas that need to be improved.

Self-reflection

Self-reflection is the most popular form of review as it takes very little time and can be carried out at any point appropriate for that sports leader. Most sports leaders carry out a self-reflection immediately after a session because their memory of the session is fresh in their mind. This information can be captured in various ways such as writing it in a notebook or verbally recording it.

Strengths and areas for improvement

Identifying strengths and areas for improvement provides us with a template for improvement. A leader should learn something new from every activity session that they lead. It is important to consider the following areas when considering strengths and areas for improvement:
- Was sufficient planning undertaken prior to the event?
- Was the organisation on the day sufficient?
- Were there any health and safety concerns?
- What personal skills and qualities were developed through running the event?
- Were the aims and objectives of the event met?

You should also include what considerations you would need to take into account if you were to organise another sports event.

Actions and targets for future practice

For some people, it is a good idea to take part in courses to help them to achieve set targets. For example, if a person wanted to improve their skills in a certain sport they could take part in a course that is run by the National Governing Body (NGB) for that sport. Sports leaders who want to learn more about the rules for a specific sport could take part in a course for the first level of officiating which again would be run by the NGB for that sport.

To find out about courses near you, go to the NGB website for the sport that you are interested in.

There are lots of other ways that you can achieve your targets; lots of practice is always beneficial, together with feedback, so that you can continue to develop and improve.

CHECK MY LEARNING

Explain how a range of different methods can be used by a sports leader to review their progress. For each method, give some advantages as well as some disadvantages.

Methods of reviewing (2)

Considerations for review

How far the session met the participants' needs

This can be assessed from feedback during and after the session. It can also be determined to some degree by observing how the people look when they are taking part and how much effort they put in. If the participants are trying hard and looking content or focused, this is often a good sign that the session is meeting the participants' needs. However, if participants are looking bored, not making much effort or giving up, or not taking part in all of the activities, then this is a sign the session was not meeting their needs.

The physical and health benefits of the activities used in the session

Physiological impact If the session was designed to train a specific component of fitness or provide certain health benefits, the sports leader will need to determine if the participants responded well to the activities and were able to put in as much effort as possible in order to be working at an appropriate intensity. To do this, heart rate readings of the participants could be reviewed by the sports leader.

Psychological impact While a sports leader is able to gain some idea of whether the participants enjoyed the session, they would need to have some method of finding out for certain, as not all participants will smile and look happy when they are working at a high intensity. While methods of feedback are required to assess this, the sports leader will also be able to gain information on this if participants regularly return to the sport or activity session. Regular attendance will be a key indicator that the participants are gaining some form of psychological benefit from participating.

Use of technology in the session

Technology can be expensive to include in sport and activity sessions; however, many participants now have access to a range of devices that could be used to help to motivate and monitor their progress. It is a good idea for a sports leader to keep up to date with apps and technology that could be used in their sessions to provide interest and variety to the participants.

The appropriateness of components of fitness

Some sport and activity sessions are designed to train specific components of fitness to help to improve participants' performance in a sport or an activity, or for health benefits. A sports leader should consider if the training methods used have appropriately targeted and trained these specific components of fitness.

How the session met the set aims and objectives

This can be checked throughout the session by observing the participants to see if they are able to perform the planned objectives of the session, which will then help to determine if the aims have been met. By checking participant progress in drills and then again in modified games it should be clear if they have been able to achieve the main aims of the session. If the session has not met the set aims and objectives, reasons why should be explored.

What went well and what could be improved

It is rare that everything goes perfectly to plan in a session. It is important to review the parts that went well: was it due to better planning in the session plan, clearer instructions or demonstrations? When you see what went well, you can try to incorporate the same methods to avoid the things that went wrong.

When considering what went wrong, all aspects should be considered, from planning, number of participants, their age, ability, equipment used, activities included and organisation. It is important to be honest in this process and to continue to want to learn how to improve the session. This improvement may be from using a greater variety of activities, new equipment, using a different leadership style, etc.

Using review methods to get information

Different review methods have already been explored. It is important to change methods as this may provide new information to help give more informed reviews.

Using information to make the session better in the future

All the information gathered in the review should be put to good use to improve future sessions. For example, a drill may not have worked well because the participants were not organised well enough to complete it. The sports leader can assess what didn't go well and explore ways to improve it, such as organising the groups so that each includes a person of a higher ability to help to support the others, or by providing a more detailed demonstration and explanation of the drill.

Justifying skills used and decisions taken

For each session, the person leading will need to draw on varying skills, such as different types of verbal communication and non-verbal communication, to help to make the session a success. They will also need to make a variety of decisions such as deciding how to organise the participants when they are working in pairs or small groups. Whatever skills are used and decisions made, the reasons for the selection of each should be provided to demonstrate that thought and consideration was given in relation to the session and the participants.

How the session can be adapted, changed and/or improved in the future

At the end of each session, consideration can be given to ways in which the session could be adapted for future use, for example with different abilities or different numbers of participants. Ways in which it could be changed, such as using different drills or different exercises, can also be reviewed which will then help to improve the session in the future.

Recommendations for the diets of participants

A sports leader can also support participants by providing recommendations to help them to improve their nutrition for sport and activity. If a participant had a specific sport or activity goal, a sports leader could provide advice on ways to enhance their performance through nutritional change.

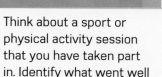

ACTIVITY

Think about a sport or physical activity session that you have taken part in. Identify what went well and what went wrong, with reasons for your choices.

ACTIVITY

A fitness leader is leading a weekly physical activity session for a group of participants over a three-month period. Explain different methods the fitness leader can use to gain information from the participants about the session to help them review their practice. Include at least one method that requires the use of technology that a fitness leader can use or ask participants to use.

LINK IT UP

How to improve diet for sport and activity performance is covered in Component 2: Methods to enhance sport and activity through nutritional change (pages 124–127).

CHECK MY LEARNING

Make a list of the key considerations for review after leading a sports activity session and provide reasons for each consideration.

Learning aim C: assessment practice

How you will be assessed

This part of the component will involve some practical delivery, leading the main component of your planned sport or activity session. You will be expected to demonstrate leadership skills and attributes in your delivery of the session. You will also need to complete a review of the activity session, using feedback from the participants as well as your teacher, and your own self-evaluation.

CHECKPOINT

Strengthen

- Demonstrate leadership skills and attributes that have a positive impact on the participants' enjoyment of the session.
- Reduce most of the identified risks from the risk assessment during the implementation of the plan.
- Select appropriate leadership styles for the target participant group.
- Use a range of methods to collect feedback from the session.

Challenge

- Show that you are able to respond and adapt the session to take into account the different needs of the participants and the selected sport or activity.
- Respond effectively to situations that arise when running the planned sport or activity session.
- Provide a justified evaluation of how successful the session was in relation to your leadership skills and attributes, as well as whether the session met its aims.

ASSESSMENT ACTIVITY   LEARNING AIM   **C**

1 For a sport or activity that you enjoy taking part in or watching, carry out research to find out about the following and how it has developed over the years:

- the equipment used
- the protection used
- the clothing worn
- the footwear worn
- the facilities used for participants
- the cameras, computers and software used.

2 Write an overview from your research that:

- identifies the equipment, protection, clothing, footwear, facilities and computing technology for the selected sport or activity
- explains how the technology has developed over the years
- explains the advantages of these developments for the participants, coach and officials
- explains the disadvantages of these developments for the participants, coach and officials.

TIPS

Before delivering the main component of a sport or activity session, work in small groups of three or four and try out your planned activities with this group. At the end of each activity ask the participants what went well and what could be improved. This will help to develop your sports leadership skills and ability to plan and lead a session. When you feel confident, try leading a group with more participants to see how the activities work on a larger scale and how your leadership style and skills will need to adapt when working with a larger group.

TAKE IT FURTHER

Explore qualifications that you could take to develop your sports leadership skills. A range of qualifications is available that will help to provide entry into working as a sports leader in the health and fitness sector.

If you really enjoy taking part in a particular sport, you could investigate coaching qualifications to help to develop your ability to work as a coach for that sport and help to improve participants' skills and techniques. You could offer to help to support your coach when they deliver training sessions to groups of participants who are at a lower level than you, to develop your coaching skills.

Glossary

1 rep max (1RM) is the most weight a person can apply in a single attempt at an exercise.

Agility is the ability to change direction at speed without losing balance.

Aim – this is a statement about what the sports leader intends to do during the sports activity session.

Anaerobic means without oxygen.

Angina is chest pain or discomfort due to reduced blood flow to the heart muscle.

Anxiety is the level of worry or nervousness a participant experiences.

Arteries are the blood vessels that take blood away from the heart.

Atria are the chambers of the heart that receive blood. Atria is the plural term for this structure and atrium is the term for the singular structure.

Blood pressure – the heart pumps the blood through a system of blood vessels which needs to be at a certain pressure to ensure that the blood is able to travel all around the body and return back to the heart.

Blood viscosity is the thickness of the blood. Viscosity is how thick a liquid is. For example, water has a very low viscosity but syrup has a high viscosity.

Body composition is the relative ratio of fat mass to fat-free mass. Fat-free mass consists of the vital organs, such as the heart and lungs, muscle tissue and bone.

A **calorie** is a measure of the energy in a food.

Capillarisation is the process where new capillaries are formed at the alveoli in the lungs and at the skeletal muscle.

Cardiac hypertrophy is where the heart muscle increases in size.

Clot – also known as a scab which forms over wounded tissue to prevent excess blood loss from damaged blood vessels.

Core muscles are the abdominal muscles, back muscles and muscles around the pelvis.

Diffusion is the free movement of particles from areas of high concentration to areas of low concentration.

Dynamic exercise is an exercise that involves movement at a joint.

Dynamic stretching involves movement at a joint.

Expiration means breathing air out.

Flexibility is the range of motion available at the joints of the body. It includes the ability of a person to move a joint fluidly through its complete range of movement.

Fortified foods have vitamins or minerals added to them which do not naturally occur in that food. For example, vitamin D is often added to milk. This is to help to improve nutrition and prevent any vitamin or mineral deficiencies.

Gait means how a person walks, jogs or runs.

Gaseous exchange is the process of oxygen diffusing into or out of the bloodstream and carbon dioxide diffusing into or out of the bloodstream.

A **goal** is something an individual wants to achieve.

Hand-eye coordination means the control of hand movements using visual input to guide the movements of the hand.

Hazard is something that has the potential to cause injury.

A **heart attack** can happen when blood flow to the heart muscle is stopped and the heart muscle tissue begins to die.

High impact means a sport or activity which involves both feet leaving the ground, which places stress on the body. Examples of high impact activities are jogging and jumping.

High impact involves an activity that involves both feet leaving the ground, such as running and jumping.

High intensity involves taking part in an activity that raises your heart rate to a high level, such as cycling at a very fast rate or up a steep hill.

Homophobic describes a form of prejudice against homosexual people.

Hypertension means high blood pressure.

Hypertrophy means an increase in muscle size.

Inspiration means breathing air in.

Intangible means something that does not have a physical presence, that can't be seen or touched.

Intensity means how hard a person is working or how much effort they put into something.

Intersex means a person born with both male and female sex characteristics.

Isotonic is a solution that has the same osmotic pressure as the body's fluids. This essentially means it has a similar concentration of dissolved solids as our blood.

Left ventricle – pumps blood to tissues all over the body. The right ventricle only pumps blood to the lungs.

Ligaments join bone to bone.

Load is the weight lifted or the resistance a person is working against.

Long-term effects usually mean a person has been taking part in regular training for six weeks or longer.

Low impact involves one or both feet being in contact with the ground such as walking.

Low intensity involves an activity that raises your heart rate to a low-to-moderate level, such as walking.

Macro means large. Macronutrients should be eaten in large quantities.

Macronutrients are nutrients that are needed in large amounts and contain energy.

Maximal inspiration is the most amount of air that a person can breathe in during a breath.

Maximum heart rate is estimated as 220 minus the person's age.

Metal composite is a material made from a mixture of materials, often graphite or carbon mixed with other materials, like titanium and Kevlar®. Composite tennis rackets are made out of layers of different materials, usually graphite and fibreglass, mixed with other materials like Kevlar, or a material similar to fibreglass that contains ceramic particles.

Micro means small. Micronutrients should be eaten in small quantities.

Micronutrients are needed in smaller amounts and contain no energy.

Muscle hypertrophy is where the muscle tissue increases in size.

Muscular endurance is where a muscle can continue contracting over a period of time against a light-to moderate fixed resistance or load.

Non-verbal communication involves using methods of communication other than speaking.

Normative data shows what is usually expected for a specific population.

Objective – this is a statement, or set of statements, that define measurable outcomes.

Osteoporosis – if a person has osteoporosis it means their bones are not very strong and more likely to fracture.

Pliable means an increase in the ability to stretch without breaking.

Positional awareness is the awareness of the physical position in which a person is located.

Psychology is made up of two parts: ology means 'the study of' and psyche means the 'human mind'; therefore psychology is the study of the human mind.

Reliability is the repeatability of results. If the test is repeated in exactly the same way, the same results should be achieved.

Repetitions (**reps**) are the number of times a movement is repeated.

Resistance training is undertaking exercise or activity to improve muscular strength and/or endurance by using weights, your own bodyweight or, for example, elastic bands, to provide resistance to the muscles.

Risk is an injury or harm that could happen to a person in response to a hazard.

Risk assessment is a list of possible hazards and risks associated with each hazard which shows the likelihood of them happening, and methods to reduce the risk.

Rupture means to break or burst. When blood vessels are burst, blood that was being carried in the blood vessels leaks out in the surrounding cells.

Sets are how often a group of reps is completed.

Slipped disc – a disc is positioned between each vertebra in the spine to act as a shock absorber. If the disc slips, it moves out of its correct position and can press on nerves in the spine which can cause numbness or pain along the affected nerve.

Spasticity is where muscles become very stiff and tight, which results in them being able to perform very restricted movements.

Sport-specific drills are exercises used to develop sporting techniques used in specific sports.

Static stretching is stationary.

Strength is the maximum force (in kg or N) that can be generated by a muscle or muscle group during a single contraction.

Strength is the maximum force (in kg or N) that can be generated by a muscle or muscle group.

Sustained physical activity means exercising at a moderate to high intensity for 30 minutes or longer.

Sweet spot is the best place on the racket head to hit the ball.

Tangible means something that has a physical presence, i.e. it can be seen and/or touched and usually has some form of financial value.

Tendons join muscles to bone.

Transgender means a person who does not identify with their birth sex.

Transphobic describes a form of prejudice against transgender people.

Vasoconstriction refers to a decrease in the size of a blood vessel.

Vasoconstriction is when the diameter of a blood vessel decreases in size to reduce blood flow through it

Vasodilation – vaso means blood vessel, dilation means increase in size.

A **vegan** is a person who does not eat meat, fish or any foods that come from an animal such as eggs or milk.

A **vegetarian** is a person who does not eat meat or fi sh.

Veins are the blood vessels that return blood to the heart.

Ventricles are the chambers of the heart that pump blood out of the heart.

Verbal communication is where a person speaks to another person or group of people.

Vital capacity is the amount of air that can be forced out of the lungs after **maximal inspiration**.

Index